☑ **W9-AYD-927**

Grade **4**

Scott Foresman

Weekly Tests
Teacher's Manual

PEARSON

Glenview, Illinois • Boston, Massachusetts • Chandler, Arizona • Upper Saddle River, New Jersey

The Pearson Promise

As the largest educational publishing company in the world, Pearson is committed to providing you with curriculum that not only meets the Common Core State Standards, but also supports your implementation of these standards with your students.

Pearson has aligned the Common Core State Standards to every grade level of *Scott Foresman Reading Street,* our premier educational curriculum. This product provides an alignment of the Common Core State Standards to the Grade 4 assessment items in *Scott Foresman Reading Street Weekly Tests.*

We value your partnership highly and look forward to continuing our mission to provide educational materials that fully satisfy your classroom needs.

ISBN-13: 978-0-328-68133-4
ISBN-10:   0-328-68133-4
1 2 3 4 5 6 7 8 9 10 V001 15 14 13 12 11

CONTENTS

Unit 1 Turning Points

Unit 2 Teamwork

Unit 3 Patterns in Nature

Unit 4 Puzzles and Mysteries

Unit 5 Adventures by Land, Air, and Water

Unit 6 Reaching for Goals

OVERVIEW

The Weekly Tests are an important part of the wide array of formal tests and classroom assessments that support instruction in Scott Foresman *Reading Street*. These tests are designed to measure student progress based on the vocabulary, word analysis, comprehension, and writing skills taught each week. Progress on the Weekly Tests is critical for determining whether the student is mastering the weekly target skills.

This Teacher's Manual includes the following: (1) a description of the Weekly Tests, (2) instructions for administering the tests, (3) instructions for scoring and recording test results, (4) reproducible charts on which to track the progress of your students, (5) the answers to the tests, and (6) alignments to the Common Core State Standards (in the Item Analysis charts and at the bottom of each student test page).

DESCRIPTION OF THE WEEKLY TESTS

In Grade 4, there are 30 tests—one for each week in the Scott Foresman *Reading Street* program.

Each test contains 4 subtests:

- The **Vocabulary** subtest consists of 5–7 multiple-choice questions that assess student knowledge of the week's selection vocabulary words.

- The **Word Analysis** subtest consists of 5–7 multiple-choice questions that assess student understanding of the week's word analysis skill.

- The **Comprehension** subtest consists of a reading passage and 8 multiple-choice questions. At least 5 of the questions assess the week's target comprehension skill. At least 1 question assesses the week's review comprehension skill. Some tests also contain 1 or 2 questions that assess other reading comprehension skills.

- The **Writing** subtest consists of a writing prompt that asks students to respond to the main selection in the Student Edition.

ADMINISTERING THE WEEKLY TESTS

The Weekly Tests should be administered at the end of Day 5 in each week.

These tests are not intended to be timed. However, for the purposes of scheduling, planning, and practicing for timed-test situations, the tests can be administered in 45 minutes—approximately 15 minutes for the Vocabulary and Word Analysis subtests, 15 minutes for the Comprehension subtest, and 15 minutes for the Writing subtest.

SCORING THE WEEKLY TESTS

Answer keys for the Weekly Tests begin on page 1. Refer to the answer key for the test you are scoring and mark each multiple-choice question as either correct (1 point) or incorrect (0 points). To score the Writing subtest, refer to the rubrics that begin on page T19.

When you have finished scoring a student's test, complete the appropriate row on the Student Progress Chart and the Class Progress Chart. Doing so allows you to keep track of your students' total scores as well as their scores on each of the individual subtests. The chart can also help you monitor your students' progress throughout the year.

The target comprehension skill of the week is the skill whose standard has at least 5 questions dedicated to it on the Reading Comprehension subtest. To assess whether a student has mastered the skill on a particular test, look at the number of items the student had correct. If the student missed more than 1 question on the target comprehension skill of the week, then the student needs reteaching and more practice. Refer to the Item Analysis chart that begins on page T9 to identify the skills assessed on each test and the Common Core State Standard aligned to each skill.

RETEACHING OPTIONS

If a student performs poorly on a Weekly Test or shows a lack of adequate progress during the year, use the Review lessons in the Scott Foresman *Reading Street* Teacher's Editions and provide the student with additional opportunities to practice the selection vocabulary and target skills.

Scott Foresman *Reading Street*
Student Weekly Test Progress Chart—Grade 4

Student Name: _____

Test	Vocabulary	Phonics/Word Analysis	Comprehension	Multiple-Choice Total	Writing	TOTAL
Weekly Test 1	/7	/5	/8	/20		
Weekly Test 2	/6	/6	/8	/20		
Weekly Test 3	/7	/5	/8	/20		
Weekly Test 4	/7	/5	/8	/20		
Weekly Test 5	/7	/5	/8	/20		
Weekly Test 6	/7	/5	/8	/20		
Weekly Test 7	/5	/7	/8	/20		
Weekly Test 8	/7	/5	/8	/20		
Weekly Test 9	/7	/5	/8	/20		
Weekly Test 10	/7	/5	/8	/20		
Weekly Test 11	/7	/5	/8	/20		
Weekly Test 12	/6	/6	/8	/20		
Weekly Test 13	/5	/7	/8	/20		
Weekly Test 14	/6	/6	/8	/20		
Weekly Test 15	/7	/5	/8	/20		
Weekly Test 16	/7	/5	/8	/20		
Weekly Test 17	/7	/5	/8	/20		
Weekly Test 18	/7	/5	/8	/20		
Weekly Test 19	/7	/5	/8	/20		
Weekly Test 20	/7	/5	/8	/20		
Weekly Test 21	/7	/5	/8	/20		
Weekly Test 22	/7	/5	/8	/20		
Weekly Test 23	/7	/5	/8	/20		
Weekly Test 24	/7	/5	/8	/20		
Weekly Test 25	/7	/5	/8	/20		
Weekly Test 26	/7	/5	/8	/20		
Weekly Test 27	/6	/6	/8	/20		
Weekly Test 28	/7	/5	/8	/20		
Weekly Test 29	/6	/6	/8	/20		
Weekly Test 30	/7	/5	/8	/20		

Scott Foresman *Reading Street*
Class Weekly Test Progress Chart—Grade 4

Teacher's Name: _____

Student Name	\: Weekly Test Total Score \: 1	2	3	4	5	6	7	8	9	10	11	12	13	14	15	16	17	18	19	20	21	22	23	24	25	26	27	28	29	30
1																														
2																														
3																														
4																														
5																														
6																														
7																														
8																														
9																														
10																														
11																														
12																														
13																														
14																														
15																														
16																														
17																														
18																														
19																														
20																														
21																														
22																														
23																														
24																														
25																														
26																														
27																														
28																														
29																														
30																														

Weekly Test Item Analysis—Grade 4

TEST	SECTION	ITEMS	SKILL	COMMON CORE STATE STANDARD
Weekly Test 1	**Vocabulary**	1–7	Understand and use new vocabulary	Foundational Skills 3.a.
	Word Analysis	8–12	Word ending -*ed*	Foundational Skills 3.
	Comprehension	13–16, 18	◉ Sequence	Literature 3.
		17, 19	Draw conclusions	Literature 3.
		20	Ⓡ Cause and effect	Literature 3.
	Written Response	Look Back and Write	Respond to literature	Writing 4. (Also Literature 1., Writing 8., 9., Language 1., 2.)
Weekly Test 2	**Vocabulary**	1–6	Understand and use new vocabulary	Language 4.
	Word Analysis	7–12	Suffixes -*or, -er*	Foundational Skills 3.a.
	Comprehension	15, 16, 18–20	◉ Author's purpose	Literature 2.
		14, 17	Cause and effect	Literature 1.
		13	Ⓡ Sequence	Literature 1.
	Written Response	Look Back and Write	Respond to literature	Writing 2.b. (Also Writing 4., 5., Language 1., 2.)
Weekly Test 3	**Vocabulary**	1–7	Understand and use new vocabulary	Language 4.
	Word Analysis	8–12	Word ending -*ing*	Foundational Skills 3.a.
	Comprehension	13–16, 18	◉ Literary elements: Character, setting, plot	13, 16: Literature 1. 18: Literature 3.
		19, 20	Draw conclusions	Literature 3.
		17	Ⓡ Sequence	Literature 1.
	Written Response	Look Back and Write	Respond to literature	Writing 4. (Also Literature 3., Writing 3., 3.d., Language 1., 2.)

Weekly Test Item Analysis—Grade 4

TEST	SECTION	ITEMS	SKILL	COMMON CORE STATE STANDARD
Weekly Test 4	**Vocabulary**	1–7	Understand and use new vocabulary	Language 4.
	Word Analysis	8–12	Compound words	Language 4.
	Comprehension	14, 16, 18, 19, 20	◉ Author's purpose	14, 16, 18, 19: Literature 1. 20: Literature 9.
		15, 17	Plot	Literature 1.
		13	[R] Literary elements: Character, setting, plot	Literature 1.
	Written Response	Look Back and Write	Respond to literature	Writing 4. (Also Writing 3.d., 4., Language 1., 2.)
Weekly Test 5	**Vocabulary**	1–7	Understand and use new vocabulary	1, 6: Language 4. 2–5, 7: Langauage 4.b.
	Word Analysis	8–12	Related words	Language 4.b.
	Comprehension	13, 14–16, 18–20	◉ Main idea and details	13, 15, 18: Informational Text 1. 14, 16, 19, 20: Informational Text 2.
		17	[R] Author's purpose	Informational Text 1.
	Written Response	Look Back and Write	Respond to literature	Writing 4. (Also Writing 1., 9., Language 1., 2.)
Weekly Test 6	**Vocabulary**	1–7	Understand and use new vocabulary	Language 4.a.
	Word Analysis	8–12	Prefixes *un-, in-*	Language 4.b.
	Comprehension	14, 15, 17, 18, 19	◉ Cause and effect	Literature 1.
		16, 20	Draw conclusions	Literature 1.
		13	[R] Literary elements: Character, setting, plot	Literature 1.
	Written Response	Look Back and Write	Respond to literature	Writing 9.a. (Also Literature 1., 2., 3., Writing 4., 5., 9., 10., Language 1., 2.)

Weekly Test Item Analysis—Grade 4

TEST	SECTION	ITEMS	SKILL	COMMON CORE STATE STANDARD
Weekly Test 7	**Vocabulary**	1–5	Understand and use new vocabulary	Language 4.
	Word Analysis	6–12	Word origins	Language 4.
	Comprehension	15, 17–20	◉ Draw conclusions	Literature 1.
		13, 14	Main idea and details, Literary elements: Character	Literature 1.
		16	R Author's purpose	Literature 1.
	Written Response	Look Back and Write	Respond to literature	Writing 1. (Also Literature 1., Writing 4., 5., 9., 10., Language 1., 2.)
Weekly Test 8	**Vocabulary**	1–7	Understand and use new vocabulary	Language 4.
	Word Analysis	8–12	Latin prefixes *dis-, re-, non-*	Language 4.b.
	Comprehension	13–16, 19, 20	◉ Draw conclusions	Literature 1.
		17	Literary elements: Character	Literature 3.
		18	R Cause and effect	Literature 1.
	Written Response	Look Back and Write	Respond to literature	Writing 9.a. (Also Literature 1., Writing 1., 4., 5., 9., 10., Language 1., 2.)
Weekly Test 9	**Vocabulary**	1–7	Understand and use new vocabulary	Language 4.
	Word Analysis	8–12	Compound words	Foundational Skills 3.a.
	Comprehension	13, 15, 16, 18, 20	◉ Fact and opinion	Informational Text 8.
		17, 19	Draw conclusions	Informational Text 2.
		14	R Main idea and details	Informational Text 2.
	Written Response	Look Back and Write	Respond to literature	Writing 9. (Also Writing 1.b., 4., 5., 9.b.)

Weekly Test Item Analysis—Grade 4

TEST	SECTION	ITEMS	SKILL	COMMON CORE STATE STANDARD
Weekly Test 10	**Vocabulary**	1–7	Understand and use new vocabulary	Language 4.
	Word Analysis	8–12	Suffix -*ly*	Foundational Skills 3.a.
	Comprehension	13–15, 18, 19	◉ Main idea and details	Informational Text 2.
		16, 20	Draw conclusions	Informational Text 2.
		17	R Fact and opinion	Informational Text 8.
	Written Response	Look Back and Write	Respond to literature	Writing 1. (Also Writing 4., 5., 9., 10., Language 1., 2.)
Weekly Test 11	**Vocabulary**	1–7	Understand and use new vocabulary	Language 4.
	Word Analysis	8–12	Word origins—Latin	Language 4.b.
	Comprehension	13–15, 18, 20	◉ Graphic sources	Informational Text 7.
		17, 19	Main idea and details	Informational Text 2.
		16	R Fact and opinion	Informational Text 8.
	Written Response	Look Back and Write	Respond to literature	Writing 9.b. (Also Informational Text 1., Writing 1., 4., 5., 9., 10.; Language 1., 2.)
Weekly Test 12	**Vocabulary**	1–6	Understand and use new vocabulary	Language 4.
	Word Analysis	7–12	Greek roots *bio-, phon, graph*	Foundational Skills 3.a.
	Comprehension	13, 16, 18–20	◉ Fact and opinion	Informational Text 1.
		14, 17	Draw conclusions	Informational Text 1.
		15	R Graphic sources	Informational Text 7.
	Written Response	Look Back and Write	Respond to literature	Writing 9.b. (Also Informational Text 1., Writing 1., 4., 5., 9., Language 1., 2.)

Weekly Test Item Analysis—Grade 4

TEST	SECTION	ITEMS	SKILL	COMMON CORE STATE STANDARD
Weekly Test 13	**Vocabulary**	1–5	Understand and use new vocabulary	Language 4.
	Word Analysis	6–12	Related words	Language 4.b.
	Comprehension	13, 15, 16, 18, 19	◎ Generalize	Literature 1.
		14, 17	Cause and effect	Literature 1.
		20	R Draw conclusions	Literature 1.
	Written Response	Look Back and Write	Respond to literature	Writing 9.a. (Also Literature 1., 2., 3., Writing 4., 5., 10., Language 1., 2.)
Weekly Test 14	**Vocabulary**	1–6	Understand and use new vocabulary	1, 3, 5: Language 4.b. 2, 4, 6: Foundational Skills 3.a.
	Word Analysis	7–12	Latin roots *struct, scrib, script*	Language 4.b.
	Comprehension	13–15, 17, 18	◎ Cause and effect	Informational Text 3.
		16, 20	Draw conclusions	Informational Text 3.
		19	R Graphic sources	Informational Text 7.
	Written Response	Look Back and Write	Respond to literature	Writing 9.b. (Also Informational Text 3., Writing 2., 4., 5., 10., Language 1., 2.)
Weekly Test 15	**Vocabulary**	1–7	Understand and use new vocabulary	2, 4, 5: Language 4.b. 1, 3, 6, 7: Language 4.
	Word Analysis	8–12	Related words	Language 5.c.
	Comprehension	14, 15, 17, 19, 20	◎ Generalize	Literature 1.
		13	Sequence	Literature 1.
		18	Main idea and details	Literature 1.
		16	R Draw conclusions	Literature 1.
	Written Response	Look Back and Write	Respond to literature	Writing 9.a. (Also Literature 1., 2., 4., Writing 5., 10., Language 1., 2.)

Weekly Test Item Analysis—Grade 4

TEST	SECTION	ITEMS	SKILL	COMMON CORE TATE STANDARD
Weekly Test 16	**Vocabulary**	1–7	Understand and use new vocabulary	Language 4.a.
	Word Analysis	8–12	Suffixes *-ian, -ist, -ism*	Language 4.b.
	Comprehension	13, 14, 15, 18, 19	◉ Compare and contrast	Literature 1.
		17, 20	Draw conclusions	Literature 1.
		16	R Cause and effect	Literature 1.
	Written Response	Look Back and Write	Respond to literature	Writing 1. (Also Literature 1., 3., Writing 4., 5., 9., 10., Language 1., 2.)
Weekly Test 17	**Vocabulary**	1–7	Understand and use new vocabulary	Language 4.
	Word Analysis	8–12	Latin roots *aqua, dict*	Language 4.b.
	Comprehension	13, 14, 16, 18, 19	◉ Compare and contrast	Informational Text 5.
		17, 20	Cause and effect	Informational Text 1.
		15	R Generalize	Informational Text 1.
	Written Response	Look Back and Write	Respond to literature	Informational Text 1. (Also Writing 2., 4., 5., Language 1., 2.)
Weekly Test 18	**Vocabulary**	1–7	Understand and use new vocabulary	Language 4.
	Word Analysis	8–12	Related words– prefixes *im-, in-*	Foundational Skills 3.a.
	Comprehension	13, 15, 16, 18, 19	◉ Sequence	Informational Text 3.
		14	Graphic sources	Informational Text 7.
		20	Draw conclusions	Informational Text 3.
		17	R Generalize	Informational Text 3.
	Written Response	Look Back and Write	Respond to literature	Writing 9.b. (Also Informational Text 2., Writing 4., 5., 9., 10., Language 1., 2.)

Weekly Test Item Analysis—Grade 4

TEST	SECTION	ITEMS	SKILL	COMMON CORE STATE STANDARD
Weekly Test 19	**Vocabulary**	1–7	Understand and use new vocabulary	1–4, 6, 7: Language 4.b. 5: Language 4.
	Word Analysis	8–12	Greek and Latin prefixes *trans-, tele-*	Language 4.b.
	Comprehension	13, 15, 16, 18, 19	◎ Graphic sources	Informational Text 7.
		14, 20	Main idea and details	Informational Text 1.
		17	R Compare and contrast	Informational Text 1.
	Written Response	Look Back and Write	Respond to literature	Writing 9.b. (Also Informational Text 1., Writing 2., 4., 5., 9., Language 1., 2.)
Weekly Test 20	**Vocabulary**	1–7	Understand and use new vocabulary	Language 5.c.
	Word Analysis	8–12	Greek prefixes *amphi-, anti-*	Language 4.b.
	Comprehension	14, 15, 17, 18, 20	◎ Literary elements: Character and plot	Literature 1.
		16, 19	Draw conclusions	Literature 1.
		13	R Compare and contrast	Literature 1.
	Written Response	Look Back and Write	Respond to literature	Writing 9.a. (Also Literature 1., 3., Writing 4., 5., 10., Language 1., 2.)
Weekly Test 21	**Vocabulary**	1–7	Understand and use new vocabulary	1: Language 1.g. 2–7: Foundational Skills 3.a.
	Word Analysis	8–12	French word origins	Language 4.a.
	Comprehension	15–17, 19, 20	◎ Author's purpose	Informational Text 8.
		14, 18	Draw conclusions	Informational Text 1.
		13	R Graphic sources	Informational Text 7.
	Written Response	Look Back and Write	Respond to literature	Writing 1.a. (Also Writing 5., Language 1., 2.)

Weekly Test Item Analysis—Grade 4

TEST	SECTION	ITEMS	SKILL	COMMON CORE STATE STANDARD
Weekly Test 22	**Vocabulary**	1–7	Understand and use new vocabulary	1–6: Language 4.b. 7: Foundational Skills 3.a.
	Word Analysis	8–12	Suffixes *-ous, -able, -ible*	Language 4.b.
	Comprehension	13, 15, 17–19	◉ Compare and contrast	Informational Text 1.
		14, 16, 20	**R** Literary elements: Character and plot	Informational Text 1.
	Written Response	Look Back and Write	Respond to literature	Writing 1. (Also Informational Text 1., Writing 2., 4., 5., 9., Language 1., 2.)
Weekly Test 23	**Vocabulary**	1–7	Understand and use new vocabulary	Language 4.
	Word Analysis	8–12	Related words	Language 4.a.
	Comprehension	13, 15, 16, 17, 20	◉ Literary elements: Character, plot, and theme	13, 15–17: Literature 3. 20: Literature 2.
		14, 18	Sequence	Literature 3.
		19	**R** Author's purpose	Literature 2.
	Written Response	Look Back and Write	Respond to literature	Writing 4. (Also Writing 3.d., Language 1., 2.)
Weekly Test 24	**Vocabulary**	1–7	Understand and use new vocabulary	1–3, 5–7: Foundational Skills 3.a. 4: Language 4.
	Word Analysis	8–12	Suffix *-ion*	Language 4.b.
	Comprehension	13, 14, 17, 18, 20	◉ Main idea and details	Informational Text 2.
		15, 16	Draw conclusions	Informational Text 1.
		19	**R** Fact and opinion	Informational Text 1.
	Written Response	Look Back and Write	Respond to literature	Writing 2. (Also Informational Text 3., Language 1., 2.)

Weekly Test Item Analysis—Grade 4

TEST	SECTION	ITEMS	SKILL	COMMON CORE STATE STANDARD
Weekly Test 25	**Vocabulary**	1–7	Understand and use new vocabulary	Language 5.c.
	Word Analysis	8–12	German word origins	Language 4.a.
	Comprehension	15–19	◉ Draw conclusions	Literature 3.
		13, 14	Sequence	Literature 3.
		20	**R** Literary elements: Character, plot, and theme	Literature 2.
	Written Response	Look Back and Write	Respond to literature	Literature 3. (Also Writing 2. Language 1., 2.)
Weekly Test 26	**Vocabulary**	1–7	Understand and use new vocabulary	1–3, 6, 7: Language 4.b. 4, 5: Foundational Skills 3.a.
	Word Analysis	8–12	Latin roots *gener, port*	Language 4.b.
	Comprehension	13, 15, 17, 19, 20	◉ Cause and effect	Informational Text 3.
		14, 18	Draw conclusions	Informational Text 3.
		16	**R** Main idea and details	Informational Text 3.
	Written Response	Look Back and Write	Respond to literature	Writing 2.b. (Also Informational Text 1. Writing 2., 4., 5., Language 1., 2.)
Weekly Test 27	**Vocabulary**	1–6	Understand and use new vocabulary	Language 4.
	Word Analysis	7–12	Latin roots *dur, ject*	Language 4.b.
	Comprehension	14–16, 18, 19	◉ Fact and opinion	Informational Text 1.
		13, 20	Main idea and details	Informational Text 2.
		17	**R** Draw conclusions	Informational Text 2.
	Written Response	Look Back and Write	Respond to literature	Informational Text 7. (Also Writing 2., 2.b., 4., 5. Language 1., 2.)

Weekly Test Item Analysis—Grade 4

TEST	SECTION	ITEMS	SKILL	COMMON CORE STATE STANDARD
Weekly Test 28	**Vocabulary**	1–7	Understand and use new vocabulary	Foundational Skills 4.c.
	Word Analysis	8–12	French word origins	Language 4.
	Comprehension	13, 14, 18–20	◉ Sequence	Literature 1.
		16, 17	Draw conclusions	Literature 1.
		15	**R** Compare and contrast	Literature 1.
	Written Response	Look Back and Write	Respond to literature	Literature 3. (Also Literature 1., Writing 2., 4., 5. Language 1., 2.)
Weekly Test 29	**Vocabulary**	1–6	Understand and use new vocabulary	Language 4.
	Word Analysis	7–12	Related words	Language 4.
	Comprehension	13–15, 17, 18	◉ Generalize	Literature 1.
		19, 20	Draw conclusions	Literature 1.
		16	**R** Sequence	Literature 1.
	Written Response	Look Back and Write	Respond to literature	Literature 5. (Also Writing 2., 4., 5., Language 1., 2.)
Weekly Test 30	**Vocabulary**	1–7	Understand and use new vocabulary	Foundational Skills 4.c.
	Word Analysis	8–12	Prefixes *astro-*, Greek and Latin roots	Language 4.b.
	Comprehension	13, 15, 17, 18, 20	◉ Graphic sources	Informational Text 7.
		14, 19	Draw conclusions	Informational Text 3.
		16	**R** Generalize	Informational Text 3.
	Written Response	Look Back and Write	Respond to literature	Writing 2.b. (Also Informational Text 3., Writing 2., 4., 5. Language 1., 2.)

COMPREHENSION TARGET SKILL COVERAGE

How can the Weekly Tests predict student success on Unit Benchmark Tests?

Each Unit Benchmark Test, as well as assessing overall student reading ability, concentrates on two skills taught and/or reviewed during the unit by including several questions on those skills. In order to ensure that comprehension target skill can be accurately learned and then tested, students learn each target skill through a combination of being taught and reviewing the skill multiple times before testing occurs. The charts below show the units/weeks where the target comprehension skills are taught and where they are tested on Weekly Tests. Based on the student's number of correct answers for each tested target skill, the teacher will know whether a student has gained the necessary skill knowledge before the Unit Test is given. A low score on the Weekly Tests probably indicates a need for closer review of the student's performance and perhaps additional instruction. It is important to understand that these tests provide only one look at the student's progress and should be interpreted in conjunction with other assessments and the teacher's observation.

Using the Comprehension Target Skill Coverage Chart

To score target skill knowledge, use the Comprehension Target Skill Coverage Chart.

1. Make a copy of the appropriate Comprehension Target Skill Coverage chart for each student.

2. To score, circle the number of correct answers the student had for that skill on the appropriate Weekly Test.

3. Using the total number of correct answers for a skill, check the appropriate box under *Student Trend* to indicate whether or not the student has acquired the target skill knowledge. We recommend 90% correct as the criterion for skill acquisition at this level. Add any notes or observations that may be helpful to you and the student in later instruction.

GRADE 4 — COMPREHENSION TARGET SKILL COVERAGE CHART

Student Name _____

Unit 1 Tested Skills	Weekly Test Locations	Number Correct	Student Trend
Sequence	Weekly Test 1	0 1 2 3 4 5	____ Skill knowledge acquired ____ Skill needs further review
	Weekly Test 2	0 1	
	Weekly Test 3	0 1	
Author's Purpose	Weekly Test 2	0 1 2 3 4 5	____ Skill knowledge acquired ____ Skill needs further review
	Weekly Test 4	0 1 2 3 4 5	
	Weekly Test 5	0 1	

Unit 2 Tested Skills	Weekly Test Locations	Number Correct	Student Trend
Draw Conclusions	Weekly Test 1	0 1 2	
	Weekly Test 3	0 1 2	
	Weekly Test 6	0 1 2	
	Weekly Test 7	0 1 2 3 4 5	
	Weekly Test 8	0 1 2 3 4 5 6	____ Skill knowledge acquired ____ Skill needs further review
	Weekly Test 9	0 1 2	
	Weekly Test 10	0 1 2	
Main Idea and Supporting Details	Weekly Test 5	0 1 2 3 4 5 6 7	____ Skill knowledge acquired ____ Skill needs further review
	Weekly Test 7	0 1	
	Weekly Test 9	0 1	
	Weekly Test 10	0 1 2 3 4 5	

GRADE 4 — COMPREHENSION TARGET SKILL COVERAGE CHART

Student Name _____

Unit 3 Tested Skills	Weekly Test Locations	Number Correct	Student Trend
Fact and Opinion	Weekly Test 9	0 1 2 3 4 5	_____ Skill knowledge acquired _____ Skill needs further review
	Weekly Test 10	0 1	
	Weekly Test 11	0 1	
	Weekly Test 12	0 1 2 3 4 5	
Generalize	Weekly Test 13	0 1 2 3 4 5	_____ Skill knowledge acquired _____ Skill needs further review
	Weekly Test 15	0 1 2 3 4 5	

Unit 4 Tested Skills	Weekly Test Locations	Number Correct	Student Trend
Compare and Contrast	Weekly Test 16	0 1 2 3 4 5	_____ Skill knowledge acquired _____ Skill needs further review
	Weekly Test 17	0 1 2 3 4 5	
	Weekly Test 19	0 1	
	Weekly Test 20	0 1	
Cause and Effect	Weekly Test 1	0 1	
	Weekly Test 2	0 1 2	
	Weekly Test 6	0 1 2 3 4 5	
	Weekly Test 8	0 1	
	Weekly Test 13	0 1 2	
	Weekly Test 14	0 1 2 3 4 5	_____ Skill knowledge acquired _____ Skill needs further review
	Weekly Test 16	0 1	
	Weekly Test 17	0 1 2	

GRADE 4 — COMPREHENSION TARGET SKILL COVERAGE CHART

Student Name _____

Unit 5 Tested Skills	Weekly Test Locations	Number Correct	Student Trend
Author's Purpose	Weekly Test 2	0 1 2 3 4 5	
	Weekly Test 4	0 1 2 3 4 5	
	Weekly Test 5	0 1	
	Weekly Test 7	0 1	_____ Skill knowledge acquired
	Weekly Test 21	0 1 2 3 4 5	_____ Skill needs further review
	Weekly Test 23	0 1	
Literary Elements: Character/Plot/Theme	Weekly Test 3	0 1 2 3	
	Weekly Test 4	0 1 2 3	
	Weekly Test 6	0 1	
	Weekly Test 7	0 1 2	
	Weekly Test 8	0 1	
	Weekly Test 20	0 1 2 3 4 5	
	Weekly Test 22	0 1 2 3	_____ Skill knowledge acquired
	Weekly Test 23	0 1 2 3 4 5	_____ Skill needs further review
	Weekly Test 25	0 1	

Student Name _____

Unit 6 Tested Skills	Weekly Test Locations	Number Correct	Student Trend
Fact and Opinion	Weekly Test 9	0 1 2 3 4 5	
	Weekly Test 10	0 1	
	Weekly Test 11	0 1	
	Weekly Test 12	0 1 2 3 4 5	_____ Skill knowledge acquired
	Weekly Test 24	0 1	
	Weekly Test 27	0 1 2 3 4 5	_____ Skill needs further review
Graphic Sources	Weekly Test 11	0 1 2 3 4 5	
	Weekly Test 12	0 1	
	Weekly Test 14	0 1	
	Weekly Test 18	0 1	
	Weekly Test 19	0 1 2 3 4 5	_____ Skill knowledge acquired
	Weekly Test 21	0 1	
	Weekly Test 30	0 1 2 3 4 5	_____ Skill needs further review

SCORING RUBRICS FOR WRITING

Use one of the following rubrics (2 points or 4 points depending on your needs) to evaluate student responses on the Writing subtest. Suggested top-score responses for each week's prompt follow the rubrics.

Two-Point Scoring Rubric

2 points:

The response indicates that the student has a complete understanding of the reading concept embodied in the task. The response is accurate and complete, and fulfills all the requirements of the task. Necessary support and/or examples are included, and the information given is clearly text-based.

1 point:

The response indicates that the student has a partial understanding of the reading concept embodied in the task. The response includes information that is essentially correct and text-based, but the information is too general or too simplistic. Some of the support and/or examples may be incomplete or omitted.

0 points:

The response indicates that the student does not demonstrate an understanding of the reading concept embodied in the task. The student has either failed to respond or has provided a response that is inaccurate or has insufficient information.

Four-Point Scoring Rubric

4 points:

The response indicates that the student has a thorough understanding of the reading concept embodied in the task. The response is accurate and complete, and fulfills all the requirements of the task. Necessary support and/or examples are included, and the information given is clearly text-based.

3 points:

The response indicates that the student has an understanding of the reading concept embodied in the task. The response is accurate and fulfills all the requirements of the task, but the required support and/or details are not complete or clearly text-based.

2 points:

The response indicates that the student has a partial understanding of the reading concept embodied in the task. The response includes information that is essentially correct and text-based, but the information is too general or too simplistic. Some of the support and/or examples and requirements of the task may be incomplete or omitted.

1 point:

The response indicates that the student has a very limited understanding of the reading concept embodied in the task. The response is incomplete, may exhibit many flaws, and may not address all the requirements of the task.

0 points:

The response indicates that the student does not demonstrate an understanding of the reading concept embodied in the task. The student has either failed to respond or has provided a response that is inaccurate or has insufficient information.

Top-Level Responses

Weekly Test 1:

Top-Score Response A top-score response uses evidence from the text to support students' position on Miss Franny's bear story.

A top-score response should include:

- A statement about student's position on factual or fanciful.
- Details about the bear's behavior.
- Details about Miss Franny's actions.

Weekly Test 2:

Top-Score Response A top-score response uses details from the story to explain why "Bear-Dog" was a good name for Seaman.

A top-score response should include:

- The Indians have never seen a large dog like Seaman and so it makes sense that they named him by combining two words they know to describe him.
- Seaman does look similar to a bear because of his color and size. So, using bear in the name makes sense.
- Seaman also showed the Indians that he did things like a normal dog would do such as fetch and stay. So, combining dog and bear in the name makes sense.

Weekly Test 3:

Top-Score Response A top-score response uses evidence to show Pa's feelings when Laura broke her promise.

A top-score response should include:

- Pa is upset and needs time to think before he responds to Laura's confession.
- Pa is disappointed that Laura broke his trust in her.
- Pa decides that if Laura is good, he will give her another chance to re-establish trust.

Weekly Test 4:

Top-Score Response A top-score response uses details to tell about Reba Jo's behavior toward the horned toad.

A top-score response should include:

- A statement agreeing or disagreeing with Reba Jo's behavior.
- Reba Jo's problem and how the horned toad became involved.
- Reba Jo's actions to break her promise.
- Reba Jo's father's role in her behavior toward the horned toad.

Weekly Test 5:

Top-Score Response A top-score response uses details to tell about the interesting features of one of the animals in Yosemite and why it is of interest to the student.

A top-score response should include:

- the name of a specific animal that lives in Yosemite National Park
- details about the animal that support the writer's opinion that the animal is interesting
- explanation of why the animal is more interesting than other animals in Yosemite

Weekly Test 6:

Top-Score Response A top-score response uses details to tell about the boys' reactions to Joanna's being a girl.

A top-score response should include:

- At first, T.J. was disgusted.
- The boys are amazed by Jo's ability to dunk.
- The boys congratulate her and give her a nickname.
- T.J. apologizes to Jo and invites her to play with them again.

Weekly Test 7:

Top-Score Response A top-score response uses details from the top stories published in *Coyote News*.

A top-score response could include:

- The bus driver ran over an enormous rattlesnake.
- President Roosevelt's speech was broadcast over the radio, and the students heard him speak for the first time.
- Miss Byers had a big calf step on her foot during roundup, and the class had a substitute teacher.

Weekly Test 8:

Top-Score Response A top-score response uses details to tell about the importance of understanding the characters, setting, and time to understand the drama.

A top-score response should include:

- Examples of characters and their relationships to one another.
- Discussion of how the setting describes the scene in which the action takes place.
- Examples of how not knowing the characters, time, or setting would make the play very difficult to follow.

Weekly Test 9:

Top-Score Response A top-score response uses details to tell about the achievements of Gato and Mancha.

A top-score response should include:

- Gato and Mancha traveled from Buenos Aires to Washington, D.C.
- Gato and Mancha overcame many dangerous hardships.
- Gato and Mancha have a sixth sense that warns them of danger.

Weekly Test 10:

Top-Score Response A top-score response uses details to tell about the most important qualities of a President.

A top-score response could include:

- Presidents should want to serve their country as George Washington did.
- Presidents should look toward the future as Thomas Jefferson did when he bought the Louisiana Territory.
- Presidents should want to turn lives around as Franklin Roosevelt did and to make the world a better place as John Kennedy did.

Weekly Test 11:

Top-Score Response A top-score response uses details to express an opinion about whether Luke's interest in clouds was a hobby or something more.

A top-score response should include:

- A statement explaining the student's opinion.
- Luke continued his interest in weather from the time he was a child into adulthood.
- As an adult, he had a weather-watching room with books and instruments.
- He joined the Askesian Society and prepared papers about his findings.

Weekly Test 12:

Top-Score Response A top-score response uses details to tell why the whales will or will not always be part of Adelina's life.

A top-score response should include:

- A statement explaining the student's opinion.
- Adelina thinks she may be the captain of a boat that teaches people about the gray whales.
- Adelina may study to become a biologist to learn even more about the whales.
- She may be a photographer aboard the whale-watching boat.

Weekly Test 13:

Top-Score Response A top-score response uses details to tell about the three things and why they are there at the end of the night.

A top-score response should include:

- The three things are the morning star, the rooster crowing, and the beautiful songs of the birds singing at dawn.
- The morning star is the sign that night is passing and announces the birth of each day. The rooster is the watchman of the night who warns that light is coming and wakes the birds. The birds sing their sweetest songs to announce the dawn.
- The three things are there because they are gifts from Iemanjá's daughter to celebrate the beauty of her new home.

Weekly Test 14:

Top-Score Response A top-score response uses details to describe why Warren Faidley needs a safe place to stay and what he looks for in a shelter when he photographs a hurricane.

A top-score response should include:

- During a hurricane, Warren must protect himself from danger. He needs a shelter so he won't get hurt, especially since strong winds can knock over trees and damage buildings.
- A storm surge can carry seawater a long way inland.
- A shelter must be able to withstand strong winds.

Weekly Test 15:

Top-Score Response A top-score response uses details to tell how the tall tale explains changes in nature.

A top-score response could include:

- Paul Bunyan changed American forests by cutting down many trees.
- The Big Onion River became straight when Babe the ox pulled the kinks out.
- The tall tale explains that Paul Bunyan changed nature by dragging his ax and digging the Grand Canyon.

Weekly Test 16:

Top-Score Response A top-score response uses evidence to explain why Drake and Nell are a successful team.

A top-score response should include:

- Drake and Nell examine the evidence and accurately record it in notebooks.
- Drake and Nell ask questions and research the answers.
- Drake and Nell test their hypothesis with experiments.
- Because of their training as a detective and a scientist, Drake and Nell are exact and precise.

Weekly Test 17:

Top-Score Response A top-score response explains why the pink dolphin seems enchanted, by giving details about its unusual behaviors.

A top-score response should include:

- Pink dolphins are beautiful and seem mysterious.
- Pink dolphins use sonar to see three-dimensional images of things in the water.
- Unlike other dolphins, pink dolphins have large front flippers and are very flexible, so they can swim in very shallow water and even crawl onto the land.

Weekly Test 18:

Top-Score Response A top-score response uses details to tell that the Navajo code talkers were brave and dedicated during World War II.

A top-score response should include:

- The code talkers were among the first wave of troops to storm enemy positions.
- The code talkers calmly sent messages while under intense fire.
- The Navajos worked day and night during the battle of Iwo Jima without making any mistakes.

Weekly Test 19:

Top-Score Response A top-score response includes details that show Jean-François Champollion's determination and interest in the Egyptian cultures from an early age.

A top-score response should include:

- After meeting a scientist who had been in Egypt, Jean-François would stay up late reading books about Egypt.
- Jean-François filled notebooks with Egyptian hieroglyphs, imagining that one day he would be able to read them.
- When Jean-François finished school at sixteen, he had already learned all the known ancient languages and wanted to work with scholars who were studying a stone from Rosetta, Egypt, that was covered with Egyptian and Greek words.

Weekly Test 20:

Top-Score Response A top-score response uses details to describe why Chief Brown suspects Mrs. King of the theft.

A top-score response should include:

- He suspects Mrs. King because she seems fascinated with salamanders.
- He suspects Mrs. King because she told him that she has dozens of salamanders as pets and that Fred is the first tiger salamander she's ever seen.
- He suspects Mrs. King because she seems odd—she thinks salamanders are sacred creatures with magical powers.

Weekly Test 21:

Top-Score Response A top-score response uses details from *Smokejumpers* to support or deny the argument that "Extreme Risk" would have been a better title for the selection.

A top-score response should include:

- The student's understanding of what "Extreme Risk" means.
- Smokejumpers work in remote areas to fight dangerous wildfires.
- Smokejumpers use special uniforms, equipment, and tools to avoid injury.
- Smokejumpers are part of a team of people who work together to stay safe.

Weekly Test 22:

Top-Score Response A top-score response uses details to tell about why the old stone wall in Cusco was a mystery.

A top-score response should include:

- The stonework was amazing because the stones were cut perfectly and fit tightly with no large cracks between them.
- It is a wonder that the Inca could do such amazing stonework because they did not have iron tools to carve the stones, nor a wheel or animals to move them.
- It is a wonder that the wall lasted for a long time through many earthquakes.

Weekly Test 23:

Top-Score Response A top-score response uses details to tell about Axel's mountain climbing abilities.

A top-score response should include:

- Axel's mountain climbing skills are advanced. The author compares him to a track star.
- Axel knows a lot about mountain climbing from watching other climbers, especially his father.
- Axel thinks clearly and carefully about his moves as he climbs to stay safe.

Weekly Test 24:

Top-Score Response A top-score response uses details to tell about a new food discovered by the author and her friends.

A top-score response should include:

- The author and her friends tried eating krill.
- They thought it would be good to eat since so many animals survive on it.
- They concluded that krill don't have their own taste.

Weekly Test 25:

Top-Score Response A top-score response uses details to show the bravery and cleverness of Gerry's thoughts and actions.

A top-score response should include:

- Gerry helped his brother and encouraged him, even though he was scared, too.
- Gerry remembered that the sunrise was pretty slow on the moon, so they could probably make it back to the shelter before the sunlight caught up with them.
- Gerry never gave up; he dragged Vern into the shelter just in time to save his life.

Weekly Test 26:

Top-Score Response A top-score response uses details to show how Martin's father "practiced what he preached" and what his example meant to the King family.

A top-score response should include:

- Martin's father always stood up to people who were unfair to him, such as the shoe salesman and the police officer.
- Martin's father often shared his experiences with his family, teaching them to speak out against bigotry and hatred.
- Martin and his sister never forgot their father's example and spent their lives pursuing justice just like he did.

Weekly Test 27:

Top-Score Response A top-score response uses details to support the opinion that Jim Thorpe was a great athlete.

A top-score response should include:

- Jim was a star athlete in track, football, and baseball. Few people excel at all of these sports.
- Jim won a gold medal for track at the 1912 Olympics.
- Jim became a professional baseball and football player and was inducted into the Pro Football Hall of Fame.

Weekly Test 28:

Top-Score Response A top-score response uses details to tell what Miguel finds and what that discovery explains about Colonel Charlebois.

A top-score response should include:

- Miguel finds a photograph of the Colonel's old baseball team and realizes he is a big fan of baseball.
- Colonel Charlebois has a change of heart when he is invited to the baseball game because the team is named after him.
- The Colonel and Miguel's family might become friends.

Weekly Test 29:

Top-Score Response A top-score response uses evidence from *A Gift from the Heart* to show how the structure of a play is different from that of a story.

A top-score response should include:

- A play lists the characters first and tells where and when the action takes place. In a story, the author introduces the setting and characters as part of the story.
- The text of a play is written in dialogue form. A character's name is followed by words that he or she speaks, without quotation marks.
- Some text in a play is written in parentheses, indicating that these words are stage directions and not dialogue. Stage directions show how a character should move or act.

Weekly Test 30:

Top-Score Response A top-score response uses details to tell why it was important for Michael Collins to be prepared for the many jobs he had to do.

A top-score response should include:

- Collins had to make 850 computer commands in the correct order.
- Michael Collins had to pilot the spacecraft around the moon so the other astronauts could land and then return to the spacecraft.
- Collins had to be well prepared for his tasks because on the far side of the moon, he did not have radio contact with Earth and couldn't ask anyone if he forgot what to do.

VOCABULARY

Directions
Find the word or words with the same meaning as the underlined word. Circle the letter next to the answer.

1 The actor dressed in a peculiar way.

(A) strange

B bold

C normal

D stylish

2 The statue is a memorial.

F something replacing a loss

G something repaying a debt

H something rewarding good service

(J) something honoring a person, group, or event

3 The prideful father watched his son play soccer.

A worried

B protective

(C) pleased

D scared

4 My mother recalls the first time she met my father.

F forgets

(G) remembers

H celebrates

J regrets

5 Hermann Park in Houston has a grand statue of Sam Houston.

A small

B beautiful

(C) impressive

D expensive

6 I have positive memories of summer camp.

(F) good

G bad

H unhappy

J beautiful

7 Her family is selecting a new car.

A buying

B selling

C training

(D) choosing

Common Core State Standards

Questions 1–7: CCSS Foundational Skills 3.a. Use combined knowledge of all letter-sound correspondences, syllabication patterns, and morphology (e.g., roots and affixes) to read accurately unfamiliar multisyllabic words in context and out of context.

WORD ANALYSIS

Directions
Find the word that completes the sentence. Circle the letter next to the answer.

8 Kylie _____ the door open.

(F) pulled

G pulld

H pull

J pulling

9 I _____ down the street to Charlie's house.

A walks

(B) walked

C walking

D walkd

10 The captain _____ the soldiers to attack.

F commandedly

(G) commanded

H command

J commandings

11 Laura _____ the flowers along the path.

(A) planted

B planting

C plant

D planttings

12 Hector _____ his water bottle before the hike.

F fillings

G filler

(H) filled

J fill

GO ON

Common Core State Standards

Questions 8–12: **CCSS Foundational Skills 3.** Know and apply grade-level phonics and word analysis skills in decoding words.

COMPREHENSION

Rosa Parks

Rosa Parks has been called *The Mother of Civil Rights*. Many people think she is one of the most important citizens of our time.

Rosa was born on February 4, 1913, in Alabama. She spent most of her childhood in Alabama. When she was eleven years old, she went to a school for girls in a new town. Later, she stayed in the town and got a job sewing clothes.

In the early 1950s, the city buses where Rosa Parks lived were segregated. This means that black people were separated from white people. To ride a city bus, blacks first had to get on the bus at the front and buy their tickets. Then they had to get off the bus, walk outside to the back door, and then get back on the bus. Sometimes, they weren't able to get on the bus again before it drove away. Blacks could not sit in the front of the bus. They had to sit in the back. This made it difficult to get off at the right stop. They also had to give up their seats to white people if the "white section" was full.

On December 1, 1955, Rosa Parks, a black woman, boarded a bus in the early evening. She paid her fare. Then she took an empty seat in the "black section" near the middle of the bus. Soon the bus began to fill up. A few white passengers were standing. The bus driver walked back to the black section. He asked Parks to give up her seat to a white passenger. She refused. As a result, the bus driver had her arrested. Parks was tried and found guilty of breaking a local law.

Rosa's act started a citywide boycott of the buses in Montgomery, Alabama. A boycott is when many people refuse to buy a product or use a service. This boycott introduced the country to a man named Martin Luther King, Jr. He led the protest saying, "There comes a time that people get tired."

Eventually, the U.S. Supreme Court decided that segregation on city buses was against the law. In December 1956, Montgomery's buses were not segregated any more.

Over the next forty years, Rosa Parks helped make her fellow Americans aware of the history of the Civil Rights struggle. She earned many honors, including the Martin Luther King Jr. Nonviolent Peace Prize, the Presidential Medal of Freedom, and the Congressional Gold Medal. Rosa Parks died in Detroit, Michigan, on October 24, 2005, at the age of ninety-two.

GO ON

Directions

Choose the item that best answers each question about the selection you just read. Circle the letter next to the answer.

13 What did Rosa Parks do when she was eleven years old?

   A She refused to give up her seat on a bus.

   B She got a job sewing clothes.

   C She was found guilty of breaking a local law.

   Ⓓ She went to a girls' school in a new town.

14 What did black passengers on a city bus have to do after paying the fare?

   Ⓕ They had to get back on the bus in the back.

   G They had to wait on the street to see if there was room on the bus for them.

   H They had to stand at the front of the bus.

   J They had to sit in the front of the bus.

15 Before December 1956, black people in Montgomery, Alabama, were not allowed to

   A ride the buses on Sundays.

   B ride the buses on weekdays.

   Ⓒ sit in the front of the buses.

   D sit in the back of the buses.

16 What happened to Rosa Parks after she refused to give up her seat on the bus?

   F She got a job sewing clothes.

   Ⓖ She was arrested.

   H She received the Presidential Medal of Freedom.

   J Martin Luther King Jr. got angry at her.

17 A boycott is

   Ⓐ a way for people to protest something they don't like.

   B a person who breaks the law.

   C a type of city bus.

   D a law that people do not agree with.

18 Which event happened after the citywide boycott of the buses?

   F Rosa Parks went to a new school for girls.

   G A bus driver asked Rosa Parks to give up her seat.

   Ⓗ The Supreme Court decided that segregation was against the law.

   J Rosa Parks got a job sewing clothes.

19 Rosa Parks can best be described as

   Ⓐ courageous.

   B unkind.

   C unoriginal.

   D weary.

20 The author's purpose in writing this passage is to

   Ⓕ inform.

   G entertain.

   H persuade.

   J frighten.

GO ON

⌐ **Common Core State Standards** ⌐

Questions 13–20: **CCSS Literature 3.** Describe in depth a character, setting, or event in a story or drama, drawing on specific details in the text (e.g., a character's thoughts, words, or actions).

WRITTEN RESPONSE TO THE SELECTION

Look Back and Write Look back at pages 32–36. Do you think the story Miss Franny tells Opal about her encounter with a bear is factual or fanciful? Provide evidence from the text to support your answer.

The information in the box below will help you remember what you should think about when you write your composition.

REMEMBER—YOU SHOULD

☐ tell if Miss Franny's story about the bear is a factual story or a fanciful story.

☐ begin with a sentence that states your main idea.

☐ use details from the story to support your main idea.

☐ try to use correct spelling, capitalization, punctuation, grammar, and sentences.

GO ON

Common Core State Standards

CCSS Writing 4. Produce clear and coherent writing in which the development and organization are appropriate to task, purpose, and audience. (Also **CCSS Literature 1., CCSS Writing 9., CCSS Language 1., CCSS Language 2.**)

VOCABULARY

Directions
Find the word or words with the same meaning as the underlined word. Circle the letter next to the answer.

1 I do not like the <u>scent</u> of that perfume.

   A sight

   B color

   Ⓒ smell

   D name

2 The geese are <u>migrating</u>.

   Ⓕ moving

   G waddling

   H swimming

   J running

3 You can <u>scan</u> the titles in the library.

   A read word for word

   B gently touch

   C slowly move around

   Ⓓ quickly look over

4 The workers on the <u>docks</u> will load the ship.

   Ⓕ platforms on shore

   G small boats

   H large water plants

   J low reefs

5 Tasha <u>yearned</u> for a horse of her own.

   A asked

   Ⓑ longed

   C waited

   D saved

6 The ship's cargo has been moved to the <u>wharf</u>.

   F lower level of a ship

   G upper deck of a ship

   Ⓗ platform on shore

   J store on shore

Common Core State Standards

Questions 1–6: CCSS Language 4. Determine or clarify the meaning of unknown and multiple-meaning words and phrases based on *grade 4 reading and content,* choosing flexibly from a range of strategies.

WORD ANALYSIS

*D*irections
Find the word in which the ending *-or* or *-er* means the same as it does in the underlined word. Circle the letter next to the answer.

7 The <u>teacher</u> graded all the tests.

   Ⓐ banker

   B powder

   C later

   D higher

8 The <u>governor</u> sent the bill back to the legislature with his approval.

   F error

   G favor

   H color

   Ⓙ sailor

9 The <u>player</u> at third base threw the ball.

   A nearer

   Ⓑ dancer

   C layer

   D drier

10 Henry is a talented <u>actor</u>.

   F terror

   G calculator

   H minor

   Ⓙ inventor

11 The <u>officer</u> marched his soldiers off the field.

   A shudder

   B grander

   Ⓒ painter

   D soccer

12 The <u>visitor</u> left her coat in the office.

   F equator

   Ⓖ educator

   H motor

   J floor

COMPREHENSION

The World's First Rockets

The Chinese made the first rockets. But their rockets were very different from today's rockets that go into space. The Chinese may have made rockets by the year A.D. 600. They stuffed black powder into long paper tubes. When the ends of the tubes were closed, they were lit by fire. The tubes blew up. Sparks flew out of them. These rockets were the first fireworks. The Chinese shot off their rockets on holidays and at weddings.

GO ON

Common Core State Standards

Questions 7–12: CCSS Foundational Skills 3.a. Use combined knowledge of all letter-sound correspondences, syllabication patterns, and morphology (e.g., roots and affixes) to read accurately unfamiliar multisyllabic words in context and out of context.

Later, they tried something different. They left the ends of the tubes open. When they were lit, gas came out. The gas pushed the tubes up and into the air. The Chinese used them as weapons in war. A cone was put on the front of the tube. It was filled with rocks or other small objects. When the rocket hit the ground, the cone would explode. The objects inside would go flying and would hurt the enemy. A stick attached to the rocket would guide it through the air. The Chinese called their rockets "arrows of flying fire."

Most of the time, the rockets did little harm. They missed their targets many times. Even when they did hit their targets, there was often little damage. But the enemy was afraid of the rockets when they saw them flying toward them. They would run away or give up. In the year 1232, the Chinese defeated the Mongols using rockets.

One person had the idea of using rockets to travel into space. Wan-Hoo was a rich Chinese official. He wanted to go to the moon. He told his servants to attach forty-seven rockets to two kites. The kites were attached to a chair. Then Wan-Hoo sat in the chair, and the servants lit all the rockets. There was a great explosion. When the smoke cleared, Wan-Hoo was gone. His kites and chair were gone too. Some people thought that Wan-Hoo had flown to the moon in his rocket chair. Others said that the explosion had blown him up. The story of Wan-Hoo is probably just a story that people made up. But if it were true, Wan-Hoo would be the world's first astronaut!

Other groups of people made rockets after the Chinese. In the 1700s the people of India made rockets out of iron instead of paper. These heavy rockets weighed up to twelve pounds and could fly a distance of 2,600 feet. In a fight with the British, the Indians set off rockets that landed on wagons and set them on fire. The British soldiers were afraid and ran away. The Indians and their rockets won the battle.

The British soon built their own war rockets. They used them against the Americans in the War of 1812. They fired rockets all night at Fort McHenry. An American named Francis Scott Key watched this battle and wrote a poem about it. He wrote of the "rockets' red glare." This poem later became the beginning of the "The Star Spangled Banner," our national anthem.

Directions

Choose the item that best answers each question about the selection you just read. Circle the letter next to the answer.

13 Who first made rockets of iron?

(A) the Indians

B the Chinese

C the British

D the Americans

14 What was the main effect Chinese rockets had on the enemy?

F They made them fight harder.

G They killed many of them.

H They had no effect.

(J) They frightened them.

15 The author's purpose in telling the story of Wan-Hoo in paragraph 4 is mostly to

(A) entertain.

B inform.

C persuade.

D scare.

16 In paragraph 2, the author's purpose is to inform the reader about

F Chinese fireworks.

G the War of 1812.

(H) Chinese rockets used in war.

J an Indian victory with rockets.

17 The rocket attack on Fort McHenry inspired Francis Scott Key to

A escape to China.

B fight the British.

(C) write a poem.

D build his own rockets.

18 The author's purpose in paragraph 3 might be to persuade the reader that the first rockets were

(F) inaccurate but useful against the enemy.

G expensive and a waste of time.

H only meant for celebrations.

J accurate and deadly.

19 In paragraph 5 the author leads the reader to believe that

A the British army was not strong.

(B) Indian rockets were better than the earlier Chinese rockets.

C heavy rockets were not effective in battle.

D the Indians were the first people to use rockets for space travel.

20 The author's main purpose in writing this selection is to

F amuse.

G persuade.

H entertain.

(J) inform.

GO ON

Common Core State Standards

Questions 13–14, 17: CCSS Literature 1. Refer to details and examples in a text when explaining what the text says explicitly and when drawing inferences from the text. Questions 15–16, 18–20: CCSS Informational Text 8. Explain how an author uses reasons and evidence to support particular points in a text.

WRITTEN RESPONSE TO THE SELECTION

> **Look Back and Write** Look back at the last section of the story titled "Bear Dog," on pages 63–64. Do you think this was a good name for Seaman? Why? Provide evidence from the story to support your answer.

The information in the box below will help you remember what you should think about when you write your composition.

REMEMBER—YOU SHOULD

☐ explain why "Bear Dog" was or wasn't a good name for Seaman.

☐ use descriptive words to tell about Seaman.

☐ make sure you use details from the story to support your answer and explain each part of the name "Bear Dog."

☐ try to use correct spelling, capitalization, punctuation, grammar, and sentences.

⌐ **Common Core State Standards**

CCSS Writing 2.b. Develop the topic with facts, definitions, concrete details, quotations, or other information and examples related to the topic. (Also **CCSS Writing 4.**, **CCSS Writing 5.**, **CCSS Language 1.**, **CCSS Language 2.**)

- -

VOCABULARY

Directions

Find the word or words with the same meaning as the underlined word. Circle the letter next to the answer.

1 She wore a <u>ruffled</u> skirt to the party.

- A patterned
- (B) frilled
- C plain
- D straight

2 The <u>badger</u> dashed into the hole.

- (F) weasel-like animal
- G kind of dog
- H kind of cat
- J wolf-like animal

3 The cat's hair <u>bristled</u> when the dog came near.

- A curled
- B flattened
- C became wet
- (D) stood up

4 The boy wore <u>patched</u> jeans and a dirty T-shirt.

- (F) mended with pieces of cloth
- G made of fine fabric
- H having many colors
- J having many pockets

5 We sailed the boat up to the <u>bank</u>.

- A land near a dam
- (B) land alongside a river or lake
- C land that forms a bridge
- D land where money is kept

6 The ducks disappeared into the <u>rushes</u>.

- F kind of wildflower
- G nests along a bank
- H trees on a shore
- (J) water plants

7 The crayfish have <u>jointed</u> legs.

- A made of long, thin parts
- (B) made of parts that attach
- C having webbed feet
- D having hollow parts

GO ON

Common Core State Standards

Questions 1–7: CCSS Language 4. Determine or clarify the meaning of unknown and multiple-meaning words and phrases based on *grade 4 reading and content,* choosing flexibly from a range of strategies.

WORD ANALYSIS

Directions
Find the word that completes the sentence. Circle the letter next to the answer.

8 My mother is _____ me to dinner.

    F call

    (G) calling

    H called

    J caller

9 Frank is _____ for the big test tomorrow.

    (A) studying

    B study

    C studyng

    D studing

10 The teacher stopped the _____ in the hall.

    F fightting

    G faughtering

    H faught

    (J) fighting

11 I enjoy _____ in a helicopter.

    A flew

    (B) flying

    C flier

    D flyng

12 Linda is tired of _____ for the bus.

    (F) waiting

    G waits

    H waitting

    J waited

COMPREHENSION

The Perfect Dog

"Stop making that noise!" Anna yelled at her brother.

Anna's brother, Sam, was six years old. Anna was three years older. Sam often got on Anna's nerves. Right now, he was trying to whistle. It sounded like a mix of spitting and hissing. They were riding in the car with their mother. They were going to the pound.

GO ON

Common Core State Standards

Questions 8–12: CCSS Foundational Skills 3.a. Use combined knowledge of all letter-sound correspondences, syllabication patterns, and morphology (e.g., roots and affixes) to read accurately unfamiliar multisyllabic words in context and out of context.

14

Weekly Test 3 Unit 1 Week 3

Anna was thinking about dogs. Their old dog died a few weeks ago. Every night since, Anna had cried herself to sleep. She missed Chief so much. He was one of their family. Chief and her mother walked Anna and Sam to school each day. Everyone who passed by would say, "What a handsome dog!" While Anna did her homework, Chief would curl up at her feet. He slept at the foot of her bed each night. Chief was devoted to Anna and her family.

Yesterday, Anna's mother said, "It's time for us to get a new dog. I know how much you miss Chief, Anna. Chief would want us to give a good home to another dog. A new dog will help you get over Chief. "

So now they were on their way to the animal shelter. Anna's mother parked the car in front of a large, red brick building. As they walked in the front door, they heard dogs barking.

Anna walked right up to the woman at the desk. She said, "We're here to get a dog."

The woman laughed and said, "Well, I have a paper for your mother to fill out. When she's finished, I'll call Roger. He will show you the dogs."

Roger led them to the huge room where the dogs were kept. The floor was bare concrete. The room was divided into two long aisles. Each aisle had a row of large wire cages. Each cage held a barking dog. The sound of so much barking hurt Anna's ears. As they passed each cage, the dog inside would jump. It would wag its tail fiercely and bark louder. Some of the dogs were large, and some were small. Some were cute, and some were ugly. Anna felt sorry for all the dogs. "I would hate to spend all day in a cage," Anna thought. "They all need a home."

Near the end of the first aisle, Anna stopped in front of a cage. Inside was a large dog that looked like a husky. It had thick black and white fur. Its tail was curled and wagging back and forth. The dog wasn't barking. It just looked at them. It had big brown eyes that seemed to say, "Please take me." Anna put her hand on the cage by the dog's face. The dog licked her hand. Sam put his hand next to Anna's. The dog licked Sam's hand too.

"He's beautiful, isn't he, Anna?" her mother said.

"Yes," Anna replied. "I think he really likes you, Sam. What do you think of him?"

"He's perfect," Sam answered.

GO ON

Directions

Choose the item that best answers each question about the selection you just read. Circle the letter next to the answer.

13 The narrator of this story is

A first person.

B Anna.

C third person.

D Anna's mother.

14 How does Anna act toward her brother at the beginning of the story?

F protective

G kindly

H helpful

J annoyed

15 How does Anna treat her brother at the end of the story?

A She insults him.

B She acts thoughtful.

C She ignores him.

D She gets angry with him.

16 The main setting of the story is

F an animal shelter.

G inside a car.

H Anna's home.

J Sam's school.

17 Which event happens first?

A Anna sees a dog she likes at the animal shelter.

B The family's old dog dies.

C Anna cries herself to sleep at night.

D Sam annoys Anna in the car.

18 How does Anna's mother show her concern for Anna?

F She tells Anna to stop crying.

G She decides to get a new dog.

H She lets Anna yell at her brother.

J She helps with her homework.

19 Which word best describes Anna?

A sensitive

B hard-working

C carefree

D lazy

20 How is the "perfect" dog different from the other dogs Anna sees?

F He wags his tail.

G He isn't barking.

H He is large.

J He is cute.

GO ON

Common Core State Standards

Questions 13, 16, 17: CCSS Literature 1. Refer to details and examples in a text when explaining what the text says explicitly and when drawing inferences from the text. Questions 14–15, 18–20: CCSS Literature 3. Describe in depth a character, setting, or event in a story or drama, drawing on specific details in the text (e.g., a character's thoughts, words, or actions).

WRITTEN RESPONSE TO THE SELECTION

> **Look Back and Write** Look back at page 97. Describe Pa's feelings when Laura tells him that she has broken her promise to him. Provide evidence to support your answer.

The information in the box below will help you remember what you should think about when you write your composition.

REMEMBER—YOU SHOULD

- [ ] explain how Pa feels when Laura tells him she broke her promise.

- [ ] think about how you would feel if someone broke a promise to you.

- [ ] write about your ideas in detail so that readers are better able to understand what you are saying.

- [ ] try to use correct spelling, capitalization, punctuation, grammar, and sentences.

Common Core State Standards

CCSS Writing 4. Produce clear and coherent writing in which the development and organization are appropriate to task, purpose, and audience. (Also **CCSS Literature 3., CCSS Writing 3.d., CCSS Language 1., CCSS Language 2.**)

VOCABULARY

Directions

Find the word or words with the same meaning as the underlined word. Circle the letter next to the answer.

1 The cattle grazed on the <u>prairie</u>.

   A desert

   (B) plain

   C ledge

   D coast

2 Cowboys <u>lassoed</u> the horses.

   F fed with buckets

   G herded with dogs

   (H) caught with ropes

   J protected with fences

3 The dry <u>riverbed</u> was covered with rocks.

   A side of a cliff

   B top of a mountain

   C trail through a forest

   (D) channel for water

4 Please do this <u>favor</u> for me.

   F dull chore

   (G) kind act

   H difficult activity

   J magic trick

5 I hope you're not <u>offended</u>.

   (A) upset

   B surprised

   C frightened

   D unkind

6 Erika <u>shrieked</u> when she heard the news.

   F fainted

   (G) screamed

   H danced

   J giggled

7 The students made a <u>bargain</u>.

   A mistake

   B display

   (C) deal

   D mess

GO ON

Common Core State Standards

Questions 1–7: **CCSS Language 4.** Determine or clarify the meaning of unknown and multiple-meaning words and phrases based on *grade 4 reading and content,* choosing flexibly from a range of strategies.

WORD ANALYSIS

Directions

Read each sentence. Find the word that is a compound word. Circle the letter next to the answer.

8 Sally watched television on the floor of her bedroom.

   F television

   G watched

   (H) bedroom

   J Sally

9 The pitcher threw the baseball to third base.

   A third base

   (B) baseball

   C pitcher

   D threw

10 The playground was filled with noisy children.

   F children

   G noisy

   H filled

   (J) playground

11 Harry bought an expensive bathrobe at the department store.

   A expensive

   (B) bathrobe

   C department

   D store

12 Our teacher assigned homework to be done by Wednesday.

   (F) homework

   G assigned

   H Wednesday

   J teacher

GO ON

Common Core State Standards

Questions 8–12: CCSS Language 4. Determine or clarify the meaning of unknown and multiple-meaning words and phrases based on *grade 4 reading and content,* choosing flexibly from a range of strategies.

COMPREHENSION

Sleeping Cindy

Once upon a time there was a girl named Cindy. She was always sleepy. She was tired in the morning. She was tired at school. She was tired at dinner. She was too tired to go out with her friends.

"Time to get up, Sleeping Beauty," her mother would call every morning. "If you do not get going, you will not get to school on time."

Cindy would look at the clock by her bed. Then she would wonder how it got to be morning so fast. She was as tired now as when she went to bed. Nothing could keep her awake. *I've got to do something about this*, Cindy thought to herself one day. She looked in the telephone book. She found the nearest doctor and made an appointment.

The doctor was a sleep expert. He ran several tests on Cindy, but none of them showed what was wrong. "There's only one thing left to do," said the wise doctor. "You've got to find a true prince and get him to kiss you. That will take away your sleepiness."

Cindy thanked the doctor and went home. She looked up "Princes" in her telephone book, but not a single prince was listed. Then suddenly she remembered there was a boy in her class named Melvin Prince. *Could he be the answer to my problems?* Cindy wondered to herself.

The next day she stopped Melvin as he was walking home. "Are you a true Prince?" she asked him.

Melvin was surprised. Cindy had never said a word to him before. "Of course," he answered. "The Princes are an old family in these parts."

"That's all I wanted to know," said Cindy. "Now will you do me a favor?" she asked.

"That depends on what it is," said Melvin, who was puzzled by Cindy.

She replied, "My doctor said that a kiss from a true prince will take away my sleepiness."

Melvin thought Cindy was a little crazy, but he didn't say so. Instead, he shrugged his shoulders and kissed her on the cheek. All at once, her sleepiness fell away like an old cloak falling from her shoulders. She felt like a new person.

"It worked!" Cindy cried. "I'm not sleepy anymore! Thank you, Melvin Prince!"

"Anytime," said Melvin with a smile. "Whenever you need a prince, just give me a call." And he meant every word of it.

GO ON

Directions

Choose the item that best answers each question about the selection you just read. Circle the letter next to the answer.

13 What problem does Cindy face in the story?

A She can't sleep.

B She can't talk.

C She can't stay awake.

D She can't follow directions.

14 The author begins with "Once upon a time" so that the reader knows the story is

F a funny story.

G a sad story.

H a fairy tale.

J a scary story.

15 Whom does Cindy first go to for help?

A a doctor

B her mother

C her teacher

D Melvin

16 How does the author show that the story is not set in olden times?

F There is a doctor in the story.

G Melvin Prince goes to school with Cindy.

H Her mother calls Cindy "Sleeping Beauty."

J Cindy looks up "Princes" in the phone book.

17 What happens after Melvin kisses Cindy?

A She feels tired.

B She feels like a new person.

C She goes to see the doctor.

D Cindy and Melvin go to school.

18 The author uses the name "Melvin Prince" to add

F humor.

G wonder.

H romance.

J excitement.

19 The author's main purpose in writing this story is to

A inform.

B entertain.

C persuade.

D both inform and persuade.

20 What famous fairy tale has the author imitated in this story?

F Cinderella

G The Princess and the Pea

H The Frog Prince

J Sleeping Beauty

GO ON

Common Core State Standards

Questions 14–19: CCSS Literature 1. Refer to details and examples in a text when explaining what the text says explicitly and when drawing inferences from the text. **Question 20: CCSS Literature 9.** Compare and contrast the treatment of similar themes and topics (e.g., opposition of good and evil) and patterns of events (e.g., the quest) in stories, myths, and traditional literature from different cultures.

WRITTEN RESPONSE TO THE SELECTION

Look Back and Write Look back at pages 123–128. What do you think of Reba Jo's behavior toward the horned toad? Provide evidence to support your answer.

The information in the box below will help you remember what you should think about when you write your composition.

REMEMBER—YOU SHOULD

- ☐ explain what you think about the way Reba Jo treats the horned toad.

- ☐ support your answer with details from the story.

- ☐ communicate your ideas clearly so that readers are better able to understand your composition.

- ☐ try to use correct spelling, capitalization, punctuation, grammar, and sentences.

Common Core State Standards

CCSS Writing 4. Produce clear and coherent writing in which the development and organization are appropriate to task, purpose, and audience. (Also **CCSS Writing 3.d., CCSS Writing 4., CCSS Language 1., CCSS Language 2.**)

VOCABULARY

Directions
Find the word or words with the same meaning as the underlined word. Circle the letter next to the answer.

1 He photographed the <u>wilderness</u>.

   A streets that run through the center of a city

   B sand dunes that rise out of a desert floor

   Ⓒ place that is in a natural state

   D area that has been cleared for farming

2 John Muir was a <u>naturalist</u>.

   F person who comes from another country

   G person who puts out forest fires

   H person who likes to fish and camp

   Ⓙ person who studies living things

3 We want to <u>preserve</u> this forest.

   Ⓐ save

   B manage

   C divide

   D replant

4 The band put on an <u>impressive</u> show.

   F interesting

   Ⓖ amazing

   H amateur

   J expensive

5 What <u>species</u> is that animal?

   Ⓐ type

   B color

   C shape

   D height

6 We fell on the <u>slopes</u>.

   F pile of rocks

   G frozen pond

   Ⓗ sides of a mountain

   J grassy meadows

7 Can you see the <u>glacier</u>?

   Ⓐ huge mass of ice

   B high waterfall

   C deep valley

   D snowy mountain top

GO ON

Common Core State Standards

Questions 1, 6: CCSS Language 4. Determine or clarify the meaning of unknown and multiple-meaning words and phrases based on *grade 4 reading and content*, choosing flexibly from a range of strategies. **Questions 2–5, 7: CCSS Language 4.b.** Use common, grade-appropriate Greek and Latin affixes and roots as clues to the meaning of a word (e.g., *telegraph, photograph, autograph*).

WORD ANALYSIS

Directions
Find the word that is related to the underlined word in each sentence. Circle the letter next to the answer.

8 My grandfather is very <u>active</u> for his age.

(F) action

G intense

H creative

J internal

9 He will <u>resign</u> as president of the club.

A resold

B singer

C restore

(D) design

10 My sister was <u>visibly</u> upset.

F devise

G vital

H decision

(J) invisible

11 I was <u>impressed</u> by the performance.

A present

B import

(C) impressive

D explode

12 They bought a guard dog for <u>protection</u>.

F station

G program

(H) detect

J nation

GO ON

Common Core State Standards

Questions 8–12: CCSS Language 4.b. Use common, grade-appropriate Greek and Latin affixes and roots as clues to the meaning of a word (e.g., *telegraph, photograph, autograph*).

COMPREHENSION

The Pony Express

The Pony Express is part of the history of the American West. Young men rode on horses across the west. They carried the mail from place to place. It took about ten days for a rider to make the trip.

The owners of the Pony Express put ads in newspapers. One read: "Wanted: Young fellows not over 18. Must be good riders." Many young men wanted the job. About eighty of the best were first hired.

Pony Express riders had to be good horse riders. They had to cross the west safely and quickly. They covered about 250 miles a day. The riders also had to be light. The horses they rode could not carry too much. Many riders looked forward to the adventure.

There were many dangers facing the riders. They had to ride through all kinds of weather. They had to get through snow, rain, and heat. There was always the danger of falling from the horse. The rider would be left in the middle of nowhere. The horses, however, were well trained. They would often go on to the next station with the mail. Sometimes Indians attacked the riders. They were almost always able to escape. Only one rider was killed by Indians.

A Pony Express rider would start from a station and ride all day. He made brief stops at other stations. He would lift his pouch, place it on a fresh horse, and start riding again. The whole thing would take about two minutes. At the end of the day, he would arrive at a home station. Here the rider rested and ate while another rider replaced him on the trail.

Some well-known people rode or worked for the Pony Express. Wild Bill Hickok was a station worker as a young man. Buffalo Bill Cody was a rider at the age of fourteen.

The Pony Express lasted only from 1860 through 1861. In 1861, telegraph lines were put across the United States. These lines connected the country from coast to coast. Now messages could be sent in a matter of minutes. The Pony Express is gone, but it is still a colorful part of American history.

GO ON

Directions

Choose the item that best answers each question about the selection you just read. Circle the letter next to the answer.

13 The Pony Express

  A helped put telegraph lines down.

  B still exists today.

  C offered jobs to women.

  (D) delivered mail across the west.

14 What is the main idea of paragraph 4?

  (F) Pony Express riders faced many dangers.

  G Riders could be attacked by Indians.

  H Riders had to be prepared for all kinds of weather.

  J Sometimes a rider was thrown from his horse.

15 One famous Western figure who worked for the Pony Express was

  A Wyatt Earp.

  B Daniel Boone.

  (C) Buffalo Bill Cody.

  D Kit Carson.

16 Which title expresses the main idea of paragraph 5?

  (F) A Typical Day on the Trail

  G The Importance of Stations

  H The Home Station

  J The Two-Minute Horse Switch

17 The author's use of the word <u>colorful</u> in the last sentence shows that

  A he thinks the Pony Express was a waste of time.

  (B) he believes the Pony Express is a fascinating time in our history.

  C he does not respect the work of the Pony Express riders.

  D he thinks the Pony Express riders were loud and showy.

18 Why did the Pony Express end?

  (F) Telegraph lines could deliver news much quicker.

  G It was too dangerous.

  H People stopped sending mail.

  J It couldn't hire enough riders.

19 Which statement best expresses the main idea of this selection?

  A Riding for the Pony Express was a job for the young and daring.

  B The Pony Express was short-lived.

  (C) The Pony Express was an exciting part of American history.

  D Some great men of the West worked for the Pony Express.

20 Which of the following details best supports the selection's main idea?

  F Ads in newspapers brought in many applicants.

  (G) Riders faced many challenges and dangers as they rode.

  H Stations were set up for the riders.

  J Buffalo Bill was a rider at a very early age.

 GO ON

Common Core State Standards

Questions 13, 15, 17–18: CCSS Informational Text 1. Refer to details and examples in a text when explaining what the text says explicitly and when drawing inferences from the text. Questions 14, 16, 19–20: CCSS Informational Text 2. Determine the main idea of a text and explain how it is supported by key details; summarize the text.

WRITTEN RESPONSE TO THE SELECTION

Look Back and Write Look back at the letter titled "Yosemite Wildlife" on pages 151–152. Of the animals mentioned, which do you find most interesting? Why? Provide evidence to support your answer.

The information in the box below will help you remember what you should think about when you write your composition.

REMEMBER—YOU SHOULD

- [ ] write about the animal that you think is the most interesting and tell why you chose it.
- [ ] reread the description of the animal and imagine how the animal looks and acts.
- [ ] use descriptive words that will help your readers visualize the animal.
- [ ] try to use correct spelling, capitalization, punctuation, grammar, and sentences.

GO ON

Common Core State Standards

CCSS Writing 4. Produce clear and coherent writing in which the development and organization are appropriate to task, purpose, and audience. (Also **CCSS Writing 1., CCSS Writing 9., CCSS Language 1., CCSS Language 2.**)

VOCABULARY

Directions
Find the word or words with the same meaning as the underlined word. Circle the letter next to the answer.

1 Paint the <u>rim</u> first.

   A corner

   (B) edge

   C outline

   D surface

2 The travelers <u>marveled</u> at the view.

   F were filled with anger

   G were filled with fear

   H were filled with joy

   (J) were filled with wonder

3 Stretch the cloth over the <u>hoop</u>.

   (A) ring

   B peg

   C plank

   D stick

4 The kitten <u>swatted</u> the toy.

   F gripped

   (G) slapped

   H removed

   J nipped

5 Ginger <u>fouled</u> during the game.

   A stopped to observe

   B got annoyed

   (C) broke a rule

   D left the field

6 Can I borrow your <u>jersey</u>?

   (F) shirt

   G bicycle

   H costume

   J umbrella

7 Your song left me <u>speechless</u>.

   A relieved

   B drained

   (C) amazed

   D unbelievable

GO ON

Common Core State Standards

Questions 1–7: CCSS Language 4.a. Use context (e.g., definitions, examples, or restatements in text) as a clue to the meaning of a word or phrase.

Name _____

WORD ANALYSIS

*D*irections

For each sentence, choose the correct meaning of the underlined word. Circle the letter next to the answer.

8 Janet was <u>unaware</u> of the coming storm.

   F fully aware

   (G) not aware

   H aware

   J less aware

9 The answer George gave was <u>incorrect</u>.

   A partly correct

   B almost correct

   (C) not correct

   D correct

10 The home team made the visiting team feel <u>unwelcome</u>.

   (F) not welcome

   G less welcome

   H very welcome

   J welcome

11 Juanita's birthday party was <u>informal</u>.

   A semi-formal

   B a bit formal

   (C) not formal

   D less formal

12 This stamp is very <u>unusual</u>.

   (F) different

   G dirty

   H ordinary

   J old

COMPREHENSION

Penny Wise

Dan looked sadly out the window at the pouring rain. *What a way to spend a Saturday morning*, he thought. *Stuck inside with nothing to do!*

"You look bored, Dan," said his mother. "I have a job for you that I think you will like."

"What is it?" asked Dan.

"See all those pennies in the big jar in the kitchen?" asked his mother. Dan nodded his head. "Well, I would like you to roll up the pennies in paper rolls. Then we can take them to the bank and get cash for them."

GO ON

⌐ **Common Core State Standards** ⌐

Questions 8–12: Language 4.b. Use common, grade-appropriate Greek and Latin affixes and roots as clues to the meaning of a word (e.g., *telegraph, photograph, autograph*).

"Why can't we just bring the jar to the bank and get the cash for them?" Dan asked.

Dan's father laughed. "The bank won't take them unless they're rolled up. I'll tell you what, Dan. You roll all those pennies, and you get to keep half of the money." That sounded good to Dan, so he went right to work.

First he poured the pennies from the jar onto the kitchen table. Then he got the penny rolls. He made neat stacks of ten pennies each. When he had five stacks, he put the pennies into a roll. As he looked through the pennies, he found some old and rare ones and put them aside for his coin collection. He also found several foreign coins mixed in with the pennies. He put them aside too.

Finally Dan was finished. "That's a lot of pennies," said his mother.

"Forty rolls," said Dan proudly. "That's twenty dollars!"

Dan's father helped him put all the rolls into a bag. They drove down to the nearest bank. The bank teller smiled when he saw Dan take the rolls out. "Someone has been busy rolling pennies," said the teller. "How would you like your money?" he asked after quickly counting the rolls.

"Give it to us in ten-dollar bills, please," said Dan's father.

"Sure thing," replied the teller, who handed Dan's father two ten-dollar bills.

His father turned to Dan and handed him one of the tens. "That's for you," he said.

Dan stared at the ten. "Wow!" he cried. "That's the most money I've ever earned!"

"Well, let's go spend some of it," said his dad. They drove to the local ice cream shop and bought two double-scoop cones.

"Tell me, Dad," said Dan as he ate his ice cream. "How long do you think it'll take to fill that jar with pennies again?"

"It'll take a while," said his father with a grin, "but when it's full, you'll get to roll the pennies."

"That's all I wanted to know!" said Dan.

Directions

Choose the item that best answers each question about the selection you just read. Circle the letter next to the answer.

13 Why is Dan bored?

    A He is sick in bed with a cold.

    B His best friend just moved away.

    C There's nothing good on television.

    (D) It's raining, and he can't go outside to play.

14 Why does Dan's mother ask him to roll the pennies?

    F to clean up the kitchen

    (G) to get cash for the pennies from the bank

    H to find rare coins in the jar

    J to stop him from bothering her

15 Why do you think the bank won't take the pennies in the jar as they are?

    A because they don't want the jar

    B because they don't have use for pennies

    (C) because they don't want to have to count all the pennies

    D because the tellers can't count

16 How many rolls of pennies does Dan make from the money in the jar?

    F twenty

    G thirty

    (H) forty

    J sixty

17 What happens as a result of Dan's bringing the pennies to the bank?

    (A) He gets half the cash from the pennies.

    B He gets all the cash from the pennies.

    C He gets to roll more pennies.

    D He makes friends with the teller.

18 Mixed in with the pennies, Dan found

    F dimes.

    G a dollar bill.

    H some nickels.

    (J) several foreign coins.

19 What effect does the sight of the penny rolls have on the bank teller?

    A He closes up for the day.

    B He frowns, knowing he has to count them.

    (C) He smiles at Dan, happy for him.

    D He directs Dan to the coin machine.

20 Why does Dan ask how long it will take to fill the jar again?

    F He enjoys filling the jar with pennies.

    (G) He looks forward to cashing in more pennies for dollars.

    H He wants to please his mother.

    J He wants more coins for his penny collection.

GO ON

Common Core State Standards

Questions 13–20: CCSS Literature 1. Refer to details and examples in a text when explaining what the text says explicitly and when drawing inferences from the text.

Name _____

WRITTEN RESPONSE TO THE SELECTION

> **Look Back and Write** Look back at pages 186–187. When the boys discovered that Jo was really Joanna, were they pleased? Describe how the boys reacted.

The information in the box below will help you remember what you should think about when you write your composition.

REMEMBER—YOU SHOULD

☐   tell how the boys reacted when they discovered that Jo was really Joanna.

☐   write a sentence that clearly tells how the boys felt about the discovery.

☐   include details from the story to support your ideas.

☐   try to use correct spelling, capitalization, punctuation, grammar, and sentences.

Common Core State Standards

CCSS Writing 9.a. Apply grade 4 Reading standards to literature (e.g., "Describe in depth a character, setting, or event in a story or drama, drawing on specific details in the text [e.g., a character's thoughts, words, or actions]."). (Also **CCSS Literature 1., CCSS Literature 2., CCSS Literature 3., CCSS Writing 4., CCSS Writing 5., CCSS Writing 9., CCSS Writing 10., CCSS Language 1., CCSS Language 2.**)

VOCABULARY

Directions
Find the word or words with the same meaning as the underlined word. Circle the letter next to the answer.

1 Everyone participated in the <u>roundup</u>.

   A auction to sell livestock

   B contest for cowhands

   (C) herding cattle for branding or sale

   D harvest of autumn crops

2 The <u>coyote</u> crossed the field.

   (F) small wolf-like animal

   G hopping insect

   H large eagle-like bird

   J poisonous snake

3 Manny hung up his <u>spurs</u>.

   A holiday decorations

   (B) spiked wheels on boots

   C clean clothes

   D framed pictures

4 The <u>dudes</u> arrived at the ranch.

   (F) cowhands

   G police

   H villagers

   J cows

5 I hear someone <u>bawling</u>.

   A typing

   B pleading

   (C) crying

   D chattering

GO ON

Common Core State Standards

Questions 1–5: CCSS Language 4. Determine or clarify the meaning of unknown and multiple-meaning words and phrases based on *grade 4 reading and content*, choosing flexibly from a range of strategies.

WORD ANALYSIS

Directions

Find the word or words with the same meaning as the underlined word. Circle the letter next to the answer.

6 Jill bought herself a new pair of <u>moccasins</u>.

   F pants

   (G) shoes

   H gloves

   J hats

7 The man took a short <u>siesta</u>.

   A walk

   B lunchtime

   C vacation

   (D) nap

8 The chief entered the small <u>wigwam</u>.

   (F) hut-like house

   G cave

   H green field

   J forest

9 The horsemen chased the <u>mustang</u> across the open plain.

   A dog

   B cow

   C mountain lion

   (D) wild horse

10 Some houses are made of <u>adobe</u>.

   F a kind of wood

   G cement

   (H) dried clay and straw

   J a kind of metal

11 The <u>matador</u> stood in the center of the ring.

   A boxer

   B actor

   C president

   (D) bullfighter

12 At the end of the day, Miguel said *"Adios"* to his friends.

   F hello

   (G) good-bye

   H I'm tired

   J good night

COMPREHENSION

The One-Room Schoolhouse

Ellie entered the large one-room building. It was as cold inside as it was outside on this February morning. Mrs. Harper had arrived a half-hour earlier. She had started up the stove in the middle of the room. However, the heat from the stove had not had enough time to

GO ON

Common Core State Standards

Questions 6–12: CCSS Language 4. Determine or clarify the meaning of unknown and multiple-meaning words and phrases based on *grade 4 reading and content,* choosing flexibly from a range of strategies.

spread. Ellie went outside and brought in more wood. She tossed it into the stove through the iron door. *By the time the other children arrive, the room will be warm*, she thought.

The wooden door opened, and Mrs. Harper entered. "Good morning, Ellie," she said. "I forgot our lunch at home and went back for it. How are you today?" Ellie said she was well, and Mrs. Harper told her that she had something to discuss. "But it will have to wait until after school," she said. "We will have more time to talk then."

Shortly after, the students began to arrive—all thirteen of them. They were of every age and size from first grade through eighth grade. Ellie was the oldest student in the school. All year she had been helping Mrs. Harper with the younger students. With so many different grades to teach in one room, Mrs. Harper was grateful for the help.

The children went over their lessons in spelling and arithmetic. At noon, Mrs. Harper heated up the stew she had brought from home on the stove, and they all ate lunch together. Charlie Lewis gave Mrs. Harper some trouble during the afternoon session. She made him stand in the corner for half an hour. Ellie helped by listening to the younger children recite the poem they had learned. At the same time, Mrs. Harper worked with the older children. Finally the school day was over.

"Well, peace and quiet at last," Mrs. Harper said with a warm smile. "Now we can talk." Ellie sat and waited to hear what her teacher had to say.

"You have done a wonderful job helping out, Ellie," said Mrs. Harper.

"I've enjoyed it too," replied Ellie.

"I know," said Mrs. Harper, "and I'm going to miss you and the other children."

Ellie looked shocked. "What do you mean?" she asked.

"I mean that I won't be coming back to school next month, Ellie," explained Mrs. Harper. "My husband has been offered a new job in another town, and we'll be moving away."

Ellie felt like she was going to cry. "But don't worry. I've talked to the school board and told them about a fine new teacher who could take over when I leave," Mrs. Harper said. "Who's that?" asked Ellie.

"Why, you," smiled Mrs. Harper. "You're going to graduate in a short time, and I know you can do it."

Ellie could feel tears flowing down her cheeks. They were tears of joy. "Why, Mrs. Harper, I don't know how to thank you!" She embraced her teacher.

That's how the one-room schoolhouse got a new teacher—all of sixteen years old!

GO ON

Directions

Choose the item that best answers each question about the selection you just read. Circle the letter next to the answer.

13 Based on details in the story, when do you think it takes place?

   A 1600s

   (B) 1800s

   C 2000s

   D 2200s

14 Which of the following words best describes Ellie?

   (F) responsible

   G fun-loving

   H strict

   J lazy

15 Why does Mrs. Harper punish Charlie Lewis?

   A He didn't do his homework.

   (B) He was misbehaving.

   C He didn't memorize the poem.

   D He talked back to Ellie.

16 The author seems to believe that at this time

   F teachers didn't work very hard.

   G winters were especially cold and long.

   H students weren't well disciplined.

   (J) teachers did more than simply teach.

17 One way Ellie helps Mrs. Harper is by

   A making lunch for everyone.

   B dealing with Charlie Lewis.

   (C) working with the younger children on their lessons.

   D teaching science to the older children.

18 What word best describes Mrs. Harper?

   F angry

   G humorous

   (H) kind

   J clever

19 You can conclude that Ellie cries tears of joy because

   A she is happy Mrs. Harper is leaving.

   B she is sad that Mrs. Harper is leaving.

   C the room is no longer cold.

   (D) she is looking forward to becoming the teacher.

20 Based on this story, you might conclude that in this time period

   (F) many former students became teachers.

   G anyone could teach if he or she wanted to.

   H women were the best teachers.

   J there was plenty of money spent on education.

GO ON

Common Core State Standards

Questions 13–20: **CCSS Literature 1.** Refer to details and examples in a text when explaining what the text says explicitly and when drawing inferences from the text.

WRITTEN RESPONSE TO THE SELECTION

Look Back and Write Look back at *Coyote News*. What are some of the stories you enjoyed reading that made the news at Coyote School?

The information in the box below will help you remember what you should think about when you write your composition.

REMEMBER—YOU SHOULD

☐ tell which stories from *Coyote News* you liked best.

☐ think about what made the stories interesting.

☐ include examples from the stories to help your reader better understand your composition.

☐ try to use correct spelling, capitalization, punctuation, grammar, and sentences.

GO ON

Common Core State Standards

CCSS Writing 1. Write opinion pieces on topics or texts, supporting a point of view with reasons and information. (Also **CCSS Literature 1.**, **CCSS Writing 4.**, **CCSS Writing 5.**, **CCSS Writing 9.**, **CCSS Writing 10.**, **CCSS Language 1.**, **CCSS Language 2.**)

Name _____

VOCABULARY

Directions

Find the word or words with the same meaning as the underlined word. Circle the letter next to the answer.

1 The <u>script</u> is too long.

(A) written text of a play

B a costume used in a play

C a photograph of a play

D list of actors appearing in a play

2 Tom always gives good <u>advice</u>.

F witty sayings

G speeches of praise

(H) guidance

J answers to tests

3 The merchant was a <u>dishonest</u> person.

A generous and kind

B selfish

C curious

(D) untrustworthy

4 They are <u>descendants</u> of Italian royalty.

F official aides

G loyal supporters

(H) family members

J freedom fighters

5 I always let Pavel make the <u>arrangements</u>.

(A) plans and preparations

B quarrels and fights

C food and drink

D lists and directions

6 My mother and I just had an <u>argument</u>.

F meeting

G surprise

(H) fight

J meal

7 We came upon a <u>snag</u>.

A sharp tooth

B unknown type of plant

C mistake in a book

(D) obstacle

GO ON

Common Core State Standards

Questions 1–7: **CCSS Language 4.** Determine or clarify the meaning of unknown and multiple-meaning words and phrases based on *grade 4 reading and content*, choosing flexibly from a range of strategies.

WORD ANALYSIS

Directions

Find the words with the same meaning as the underlined word. Circle the letter next to the answer.

8 Please make those dirty dishes <u>disappear</u>.

(F) go out of view

G come into view

H become clean

J become wet

9 Let's <u>review</u> our plans.

A look at afterwards

B look at before

C not look at

(D) look at again

10 Please pick up a quart of <u>nonfat</u> milk.

F with fat

(G) without fat

H low in fat

J high in fat

11 It's easy to <u>reheat</u> a casserole.

(A) make hot again

B make less hot

C make much hotter

D make too hot

12 <u>Disconnect</u> the answering machine from the telephone.

F to extend a connection

G to change a connection

(H) to break a connection

J to make a connection

COMPREHENSION

from *Babes in Toyland*

Characters:

JANE, age eight

ALAN, her brother, age nine

Scene 1

Setting: An attic bedroom. Two twin beds have faded old quilts with many mended patches. There is a broken rocking chair and an old sofa with the stuffing coming out. There is one window with no curtain. The moon is shining in. JANE *sits on her bed wrapped in her quilt.* ALAN *sits in the rocker. He is wearing an old hand-me-down coat.*

GO ON

Common Core State Standards

Questions 8–12: CCSS Language 4.b. Use common, grade-appropriate Greek and Latin affixes and roots as clues to the meaning of a word (e.g., *telegraph, photograph, autograph*).

JANE: I think Uncle Barnaby is a bad man. We know he's very rich, but he never gives us

enough to eat. And why does he make us cook and clean and wash all the time? We

should be in school.

ALAN: I've been thinking things over, Janie. I've decided we have to escape!

JANE *(gasps and sits straight up):* Escape? Oh, but Alan, where would we go? I'm afraid

Uncle Barnaby would find us unless we got very far away. And if he found us, you know

he would probably never let us out of his sight again. Then we'd really be in a fix!

ALAN: Don't worry, Janie. I've thought it all through. We have to get to Toyland. Once we

get there, I know we can find friends who will help us.

JANE: Oh, that would be wonderful! I know we could find plenty to do in Toyland.

I can sew really well now because Uncle Barnaby makes me do all the mending. I can

make clothes for all the dolls in Toyland. *(Pause)* But how will we get there, Alan?

ALAN: I found a map in Uncle Barnaby's library. You know how much he hates books. He

never goes in there for anything. I found the map that will take us to Toyland. It's the

only one he had, so I took the book it was in! This way he can't follow us. *(He gets*

up and sits next to JANE.) Listen, Janie, it's a very long way. There may be danger,

and it may take a long time to reach Toyland. We have to stick together and take care

of each other. Do you think you can do it?

JANE *(with spirit):* I can do anything you can!

ALAN *(hugs her):* I knew you would say that! Are you ready to leave right now?

JANE: What? Right this minute?

ALAN: Listen. I know it's sudden, but tonight is the perfect time. You know Uncle Barnaby

went away today and won't be back for two days. We can go a long way tonight by

the light of the moon. By tomorrow morning we'll be miles into the Green Forest, and

he won't even miss us 'til he gets back. (ALAN *goes to his bed and pulls a sack from*

under it.) I thought of everything. There is food here, and I found some money in

Uncle Barnaby's desk.

JANE *(tosses her quilt aside, jumps up, and grabs her coat):* Let's go right now!

I know Uncle Barnaby will be furious when he sees the money is missing, but it's our

money after all. Our parents left it to him to look after us. So I'm glad you took it.

ALAN *(picks up the sack and takes* JANE*'s hand):* To Toyland then! *(They run out the*

door and slam it behind them. The curtain falls.)

GO ON

Directions

Choose the item that best answers each question about the selection you just read. Circle the letter next to the answer.

13 From the description of Jane and Alan's bedroom, you can conclude that

(A) no one is taking proper care of them.

B they are afraid to be by themselves at night.

C they do not like their Uncle Barnaby.

D they live in a big, beautiful house.

14 Which conclusion about Alan does the scene support?

F He has a bad temper.

(G) He is brave and smart.

H He doesn't mind hard work.

J He likes to travel.

15 You can conclude that before the scene took place,

A Uncle Barnaby searched for the children.

B Uncle Barnaby returned home.

C the children ran away together.

(D) the children's parents died.

16 Jane thinks that Uncle Barnaby is a bad man because

(F) he never gives Jane and Alan enough to eat.

G he never told Jane about Toyland.

H he cooks and washes all the time.

J he hates books.

17 Based on the passage, which is the best description of Uncle Barnaby?

A strong and fierce

(B) selfish and mean

C kind and sweet

D friendly and cheerful

18 Since Jane is wrapped up in a quilt, you can conclude that the attic is

F dry.

G dusty.

(H) cold.

J large.

19 You can conclude that Toyland is

A a place where people act like toys.

B a place that doesn't exist.

C a place where there are no books.

(D) a place that is hard to get to.

20 You can conclude that Alan and Jane want to escape because

(F) they work too hard and don't get enough to eat.

G they miss their parents and want to see them again.

H they want to live in a nicer, cleaner house.

J they want to have many adventures.

GO ON

Common Core State Standards

Questions 13–16, 18–20: CCSS Literature 1. Refer to details and examples in a text when explaining what the text says explicitly and when drawing inferences from the text. **Question 17: CCSS Literature 3.** Describe in depth a character, setting, or event in a story or drama, drawing on specific details in the text (e.g., a character's thoughts, words, or actions).

WRITTEN RESPONSE TO THE SELECTION

> **Look Back and Write** Look back at page 236. As with all plays, there is a list of characters and information about the setting and time. Why is it important to know these things before you begin reading? What might happen if you didn't know them?

The information in the box below will help you remember what you should think about when you write your composition.

REMEMBER—YOU SHOULD

☐ tell why it is important to know about the characters, setting, and time of a play before you begin reading.

☐ include details from the play to support your main ideas.

☐ make sure you state your conclusion clearly for the reader.

☐ try to use correct spelling, capitalization, punctuation, grammar, and sentences.

GO ON

Common Core State Standards

CCSS Writing 9.a. Apply grade 4 Reading standards to literature (e.g., "Describe in depth a character, setting, or event in a story or drama, drawing on specific details in the text [e.g., a character's thoughts, words, or actions]."). (Also **CCSS Literature 1.**, **CCSS Literature 5.**, **CCSS Writing 1.**, **CCSS Writing 4.**, **CCSS Writing 5.**, **CCSS Writing 9.**, **CCSS Writing 10.**, **CCSS Language 1.**, **CCSS Language 2.**)

VOCABULARY

Directions
Find the word or words with the same meaning as the underlined word. Circle the letter next to the answer.

1 The puppies played in the <u>vast</u> backyard.

   A green

   B beautiful

   C sunny

   (D) huge

2 I put the tools away in the <u>rickety</u> shed.

   F small

   (G) unstable

   H damp

   J sturdy

3 Hungry beetles <u>infested</u> the garden.

   (A) spread through and harmed

   B laid eggs in

   C helped to control pests in

   D flew past without landing

4 Stay away from the <u>quicksand</u>.

   F sand that is too hot to walk on

   G sand that is full of sharp stones

   (H) sand that is too wet to hold you up

   J sand that is blowing in the wind

5 The goats <u>roamed</u> all over the hills.

   (A) wandered

   B leaped

   C played

   D hunted

6 I felt the cat's <u>resistance</u> when I picked her up.

   F warmth

   G sharp claws

   (H) reaction against

   J ambition

7 There was a <u>landslide</u> in California last week.

   A sports match

   (B) mass of earth falling downhill

   C earthquake

   D fire

GO ON

Common Core State Standards

Questions 1–7: CCSS Language 4. Determine or clarify the meaning of unknown and multiple-meaning words and phrases based on *grade 4 reading and content*, choosing flexibly from a range of strategies.

WORD ANALYSIS

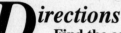irections

Find the compound word in each sentence. Circle the letter next to the answer.

8 Heidi's brother is training to be a lifeguard at the beach.

- (F) lifeguard
- G training
- H beach
- J brother

9 I felt bad when I broke the pretty, green flowerpot.

- A felt
- B broke
- C green
- (D) flowerpot

10 The hungriest person at the table always gets the last pancake on the platter.

- F hungriest
- G person
- (H) pancake
- J platter

11 I leaned my elbows on the windowsill and let the summer breeze cool my flushed face.

- A elbows
- (B) windowsill
- C summer
- D flushed

12 Tom raised an eyebrow when he heard the startling news.

- (F) eyebrow
- G startling
- H raised
- J news

COMPREHENSION

The Play's the Thing

William Shakespeare is the greatest playwright who ever lived. Shakespeare lived in London during the 1500s and 1600s. He wrote more than thirty-five plays in his lifetime. His plays are still acted today in every country of the world. But Shakespeare would not know anything about our theaters today! Things were very different when he was alive.

Shakespeare's plays were acted out in a London theater called the Globe. The Globe was shaped like an open can. It had a roof only around the edges. The large center space was open to the sky. That center space was called the pit. People who came to see the play could

GO ON

Common Core State Standards

Questions 8–12: CCSS Foundational Skills 3.a. Use combined knowledge of all letter-sound correspondences, syllabication patterns, and morphology (e.g., roots and affixes) to read accurately unfamiliar multisyllabic words in context and out of context.

pay a penny or two to stand in the pit. These people were called *groundlings* because they stood on the ground to watch the play. Groundlings made every play very lively. They often yelled at the actors. They would boo loudly when a villian came on stage. When two actors fought with swords, they would cheer loudly for their favorite.

For people who could afford higher prices, the Globe had seats. These seats were hard, uncomfortable, wooden benches. They looked just like benches in a gym. Each bench was one step above and behind the row in front of it, so that everyone could see over the people in front. There were three decks, or stories, of seats at the Globe.

There were no electric lights in the 1500s. Fire was the only source of light. Since the Globe was made of wood, fire was dangerous. The actors only used fire when they had to. Plays were always acted during the day. The sunlight came right through the big, open space above the pit. It shone on the stage and the audience. If it rained, the groundlings would get wet. Today, plays are acted in indoor theaters at night. The audience sits quietly in a darkened room. The only lights are the ones focused on the stage.

Shakespeare would never have recognized the sets and costumes in today's theaters. Most theaters spend a lot of money on furniture, design, and costumes. These are very important parts of a modern performance. Back in Shakespeare's time, actors often had to bring their own costumes. If an actor wore a plain gold crown, that was enough to tell the audience that he was a prince or a king. And there were no sets at all. Actors would bring a chair or bed onto the stage if it were needed for a scene. Audience members had to use their imaginations.

The actors themselves have also changed from Shakespeare's day to our own time. In the 1500s and early 1600s, there were no actresses. Boys played all the female roles. This was because Shakespeare's society did not think it was proper for women to appear on stage. Today, many actresses have appeared in at least one Shakespearean play. Some actresses have even taken on male roles. Sarah Bernhardt played Shakespeare's tragic hero Hamlet about one hundred years ago. Her performance was brilliant.

The theater has changed in many ways since William Shakespeare's time. But one thing has not changed. Theaters everywhere still produce Shakespeare's plays.

GO ON

Directions

Choose the item that best answers each question about the selection you just read. Circle the letter next to the answer.

13 Which sentence is a statement of opinion?

(A) William Shakespeare is the greatest playwright who ever lived.

B Shakespeare lived in London during the 1500s and 1600s.

C He wrote more than thirty-five plays in his lifetime.

D His plays are still acted today in every country of the world.

14 What is the main idea of the passage?

F Shakespeare was the greatest playwright in history.

(G) Theater has changed a great deal since Shakespeare's time.

H Theater was better in Shakespeare's day than it is today.

J People still go to the theater to see plays by Shakespeare.

15 Which sentence is a statement of fact?

A Sets and costumes are very important parts of a modern performance.

B Groundlings made every performance very lively.

C Sarah Bernhardt's performance as Hamlet was brilliant.

(D) Today, plays are acted in indoor theaters at night.

16 "If it rained, the groundlings would get wet" is

(F) a statement of fact.

G a statement of opinion.

H neither a fact nor an opinion.

J a statement that contains both fact and opinion.

17 Why did the Globe only give performances during the day?

A People would only buy tickets to daytime shows.

B It was dangerous for people to be out at night.

(C) It was dangerous to light up a wood building using fire.

D It cost less to put on a play during the day.

18 Read paragraph 3. Which sentence is a statement of opinion?

F the first sentence

(G) the second sentence

H the fourth sentence

J the fifth sentence

19 One way in which theater has changed since Shakespeare's time is that

A all female roles today are played by boys.

B people today no longer watch Shakespearean plays.

(C) most plays today are performed indoors and at night.

D theater performances today are lit only by sunlight.

20 What opinion about sets and costumes does the author express?

F Theaters today spend a lot of money on them.

G Most of Shakespeare's actors brought in their own costumes.

(H) Sets and costumes are very important to a play.

J At the Globe, there were no sets on the stage.

GO ON

Common Core State Standards

Questions 13, 15–16, 18, 20: CCSS Informational Text 8. Explain how an author uses reasons and evidence to support particular points in a text. **Questions 14, 17, 19: CCSS Informational Text 2.** Determine the main idea of a text and explain how it is supported by key details; summarize the text.

Weekly Test 9 Unit 2 Week 4

WRITTEN RESPONSE TO THE SELECTION

> **Look Back and Write** Look back at pages 268–271. What made Gato and Mancha so amazing? Provide evidence to support your answer.

The information in the box below will help you remember what you should think about when you write your composition.

REMEMBER—YOU SHOULD

- ☐ write about why Gato and Mancha were so amazing.

- ☐ make sure you support your points with details from the text.

- ☐ use time order words to show the sequence of events.

- ☐ try to use correct spelling, capitalization, punctuation, grammar, and sentences.

GO ON

Common Core State Standards

CCSS Writing 9. Draw evidence from literary or informational texts to support analysis, reflection, and research. (Also **CCSS Writing 1.b., CCSS Writing 4., CCSS Writing 5., CCSS Writing 9.b.**)

_____

_____

_____

_____

_____

_____

_____

_____

_____

_____

_____

_____

_____

_____

_____

_____

_____

_____

Name _____

VOCABULARY

Directions

Find the word or words with the same meaning as the underlined word. Circle the letter next to the answer.

1 The <u>Constitution</u> is in a museum.

   A sculpture of four presidents

   (B) document stating a system of laws

   C painting showing beautiful scenery

   D object from prehistoric times

2 Our class is learning about city <u>politics</u>.

   F headquarters

   G ceremonies

   (H) government

   J liberties

3 The event was a <u>howling</u> success.

   A celebrated

   (B) tremendous

   C particular

   D overnight

4 The girl spoke the words <u>solemnly</u>.

   F frantically

   G slowly

   H angrily

   (J) seriously

5 It is your <u>responsibility</u> to feed the dog.

   (A) duty

   B decision

   C goal

   D excuse

6 She is <u>vain</u> about her appearance.

   F jealous

   G patient

   (H) prideful

   J discouraged

7 We have a <u>humble</u> home.

   A comfortable

   (B) modest

   C decorative

   D sturdy

GO ON

Common Core State Standards

Questions 1–7: CCSS Language 4. Determine or clarify the meaning of unknown and multiple-meaning words and phrases based on *grade 4 reading and content,* choosing flexibly from a range of strategies.

WORD ANALYSIS

Directions

Find the words with the same meaning as the underlined word. Circle the letter next to the answer.

8 My brother reacted <u>angrily</u> when I lost his baseball glove.

(F) in an angry way

G without any anger

H with more anger

J in a less angry way

9 The hikers cried out <u>joyously</u> when the rescue party arrived.

A in a joyless way

(B) in a joyful manner

C with more joy than usual

D with less joy than usual

10 Amy yawned and rubbed her eyes <u>sleepily</u>.

F while still asleep

G in a lively way

H not having slept at all

(J) in a sleepy way

11 The stars shined <u>brightly</u> in the night sky.

A with little brightness

B with total brightness

C without brightness

(D) with brightness

12 The toddler walked <u>clumsily</u> across the room.

F without being clumsy

G in a careful way

(H) in a clumsy fashion

J in a less clumsy way

GO ON

Common Core State Standards

Questions 8–12: CCSS Foundational Skills 3.a. Use combined knowledge of all letter-sound correspondences, syllabication patterns, and morphology (e.g., roots and affixes) to read accurately unfamiliar multisyllabic words in context and out of context.

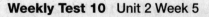

COMPREHENSION

A Joke on the General

Charles Willson Peale was an American painter. He was born in Maryland in 1741. Charles was sent out as a young man to learn a trade. He worked for someone who made horse saddles. However, his work was not good. He then tried fixing clocks. He also tried working with metal. He finally went to work for a painter. Now he found his true calling!

By 1776, Peale was earning a lot of money with his brush. He moved his family to Philadelphia. This was the largest and most important city at the time. The British colonies in America had decided to become an independent country. This meant war against Great Britain, which ruled them. Peale and his brother James both fought in the American army. Peale took part in important battles at Princeton and Trenton. He painted several pictures of General George Washington. The war ended in victory for the new country, now called the United States.

Peale had many interests besides painting. He was also a scientist, an inventor, and a politician. He held an office in the Pennsylvania government. He opened one of the first museums in America. The Philadelphia Museum included many exhibitions on both science and art.

The most famous exhibit in the museum was the skeleton of a mastodon. A mastodon is a prehistoric animal that looks something like an elephant. Peale found the skeleton in the state of New York. He and his son worked together to mount it in the museum. Many people came to see the mastodon.

Peale was married twice and had many sons and daughters. Several of them became painters and scientists. Peale's daughter Anna was one of the first important female artists in America.

In 1795, Peale painted a picture of his sons Raphael and Titan. He showed the boys standing on a narrow wooden staircase. Titan is hidden at the turn of the stairs. Raphael is climbing the stairs. He pauses to look over his shoulder at the viewer. The picture looked completely real. Peale's sense of humor made him decide to play a trick. He built a real door for his picture. He also built a real wooden step that matched the staircase. It made the whole picture look real.

Peale showed the picture to people. He waited to see what would happen. One day General Washington came to see Peale. He walked quickly through the room where the picture hung. He caught sight of the two boys on the staircase. Then he raised his hat and bowed to them. No one thought the joke was funnier than Washington himself.

GO ON

Directions

Choose the item that best answers each question about the selection you just read. Circle the letter next to the answer.

13 What is the main idea of the first paragraph?

   A Peale was born in Maryland.

   (B) Peale worked at several different jobs.

   C Peale did not like repairing clocks.

   D Peale decided to become a painter.

14 What is the main idea of paragraph 6?

   F Peale painted a portrait of two of his sons.

   (G) Peale painted a portrait that looked real.

   H Peale wanted to play a joke with his painting.

   J Peale's sons wanted to play a joke on him.

15 Which detail supports the idea that Peale had a sense of humor?

   A He was not good at fixing clocks or making saddles.

   B He was married twice and had several children.

   C He fought in the American army.

   (D) He framed his painting in a real doorframe.

16 Soon after moving to Philadelphia, Peale

   (F) joined the army.

   G began making saddles.

   H opened a museum.

   J painted a picture of his sons.

17 Which of the following sentences from the passage contains an opinion?

   A Charles Wilson Peale was an American painter.

   (B) The picture looked completely real.

   C Peale was married twice and had many sons and daughters.

   D The Philadelphia Museum included many exhibitions on both science and art.

18 What is the main idea of the selection?

   F Peale had a strong sense of humor.

   (G) Peale lived an interesting and varied life.

   H Peale fought in the American army.

   J Peale and General Washington were good friends.

19 Which detail supports the idea that Peale was very intelligent?

   A He liked to play jokes on people.

   B He fought for his country during the war.

   (C) He was a painter, a scientist, an inventor, and a politician.

   D He had several children who become scientists and painters.

20 Why did Peale open a museum in Philadelphia?

   F to give his sons and daughters something to do

   G to show his support for American independence

   (H) to share his interests in science and art

   J to play a joke on General Washington

Common Core State Standards

Questions 13–16, 18–20: CCSS Informational Text 2. Determine the main idea of a text and explain how it is supported by key details; summarize the text. **Question 17: CCSS Informational Text 8.** Explain how an author uses reasons and evidence to support particular points in a text.

WRITTEN RESPONSE TO THE SELECTION

> **Look Back and Write** Look back at pages 300–301. What do you think are the most important qualities a president should have? Why?

The information in the box below will help you remember what you should think about when you write your composition.

REMEMBER—YOU SHOULD

- ☐ tell about which qualities you think are most important for a president to have.

- ☐ explain why certain qualities are more important than others.

- ☐ . give examples to help the reader better understand your answer.

- ☐ try to use correct spelling, capitalization, punctuation, grammar, and sentences.

GO ON

Common Core State Standards

CCSS Writing 1. Write opinion pieces on topics or texts, supporting a point of view with reasons and information. (Also **CCSS Writing 4.**, **CCSS Writing 5.**, **CCSS Writing 9.**, **CCSS Writing 10.**, **CCSS Language 1.**, **CCSS Language 2.**)

Weekly Test 10 Unit 2 Week 5

59

Name _____

VOCABULARY

Directions

Find the word or words with the same meaning as the underlined word. Circle the letter next to the answer.

1 Leon scraped off the <u>scales</u> before cutting the trout.

   A side fins of a fish

   (B) thin plates covering a fish

   C gills of a fish

   D eye coverings of a fish

2 The carpenter's <u>apprentice</u> sawed the boards.

   (F) person learning a trade

   G expert at a trade

   H master at an art

   J person applying for a job

3 The student's <u>essay</u> was about animal rights.

   A kind of skit

   B make-believe story

   (C) short piece of writing

   D type of chemical

4 The returning spaceship entered the <u>atmosphere.</u>

   F area on top of a mountain

   G region of outer space

   H water in the ocean

   (J) air surrounding Earth

5 The bandage put too much <u>pressure</u> on the wound.

   A pain

   (B) force

   C heat

   D sweat

6 Kate joined a camping <u>club.</u>

   (F) group that meets for a purpose

   G group that makes laws

   H group that pays taxes

   J group that builds schools

7 The factory is <u>manufacturing</u> parts for computers.

   A putting together

   B taking apart

   (C) making by machine

   D selling or trading

GO ON

Common Core State Standards

Questions 1–7: **CCSS Language 4.** Determine or clarify the meaning of unknown and multiple-meaning words and phrases based on *grade 4 reading and content,* choosing flexibly from a range of strategies.

WORD ANALYSIS

Directions
Find the words with the same meaning as the underlined word. Circle the letter next to the answer.

8 My grandmother worked in a paper **factory**.

(F) building where things are made

G building where things are sold

H building where things are traded

J building where things are taught

9 She drew a pattern of **curves** on the paper.

A straight lines

B lines with sharp angles

(C) lines with round bends

D crooked lines

10 We agreed to **import** some products from abroad.

(F) to bring in

G to take out

H to sell cheaply

J to take care of

11 Rachel had **progressed** to the head of her class.

A left early

B stepped back

(C) moved forward

D worked hard

12 It seemed that a **century** had passed before he spoke again.

(F) 100 years

G 20 years

H many hours

J many days

Common Core State Standards

Questions 8–12: Language 4.b. Use common, grade-appropriate Greek and Latin affixes and roots as clues to the meaning of a word (e.g., *telegraph, photograph, autograph*).

COMPREHENSION

Nighttime Birds of Prey

Birds of prey are among the most interesting birds. These birds hunt and kill other animals. They eat such animals as mice, rabbits, snakes, and other birds. Most people's favorite birds of prey are owls. These birds hunt at night. Owl bodies are made for night hunting.

Owls are known for their large eyes. Their big eyes gather in a lot of light. This helps them see better at night. Their eyes also look forward. Each eye sees things from two angles. This allows owls to better sight their prey. But owls cannot move their eyes. An owl must move its whole head to look at different things.

Owls can pinpoint prey with their ears as well as their eyes. Their ear openings are in different spots on either side of the head. The ear opening on the right side is higher. Thus, the two ears receive sounds from different angles. Barn owls can use their keen hearing to locate prey in complete darkness.

Using their keen sight and hearing, owls swoop down on prey. They often surprise their prey. Their notched feathers allow them to fly almost silently. Owls fly down with their feet first. They use the talons, or curved claws, on their feet to snatch prey. Then they carry it to a perch or nest. They tear large prey apart with their talons and their hooked beaks. But they eat small prey, such as mice and small birds, whole. Hours later, they cough up the bones, fur, or feathers that they can't digest. These prey parts can be seen in owl pellets on a forest floor. The pellets are one to two inches long.

Some Common Kinds of Owls			
Kind of Owl	Length	Special Features	Call
Barn	14–17 in.	Heart-shaped face	Hissing scream
Barred	17–20 in.	Chunky shape, dark eyes	Sounds like "Who cooks for you? Who cooks for you-all?"
Eastern screech	8–9 in.	Small size, ear tufts	Trembling whistle
Great horned	20–25 in.	Bulky shape, ear tufts	Loud, deep hoots

GO ON

Directions

Choose the item that best answers each question about the selection you just read. Circle the letter next to the answer.

13 Which kind of owl is the largest?

  A   barn owl

  B   barred owl

  C   eastern screech owl

  (D)   great horned owl

14 Which kind of owl is the smallest?

  F   barn owl

  G   barred owl

  (H)   eastern screech owl

  J   great horned owl

15 What is a special feature of barn owls?

  A   chunky shape

  (B)   heart-shaped face

  C   ear tufts

  D   yellow eyes

16 Which sentence states an opinion?

  (F)   Most people's favorite birds of prey are owls.

  G   An owl must move its whole head to look at different things.

  H   They use the talons, or curved claws, on their feet to snatch prey.

  J   They tear large prey apart with their talons and their hooked beaks.

17 What is the main idea of this passage?

  A   There are different kinds of owls.

  B   Owls can hear very well.

  (C)   The bodies of owls are made for night hunting.

  D   Owl pellets are one to two inches long.

18 What kind of call does a great horned owl make?

  F   trembling whistle

  (G)   deep hoot

  H   hissing scream

  J   soft cooing

19 What is unusual about the ears of owls?

  A   They face forward.

  B   They face backward.

  C   Both ears are on the right side of the head.

  (D)   The right ear is higher than the left ear.

20 Which kind of owl has a call that sounds like *"Who cooks for you? Who cooks for you-all?"*

  F   barn owl

  (G)   barred owl

  H   eastern screech owl

  J   great horned owl

GO ON

WRITTEN RESPONSE TO THE SELECTION

Look Back and Write Look back at pages 324–325. Do you think Luke's interest in clouds was just a hobby or something more? Provide evidence from the article to support your answer.

The information in the box below will help you remember what you should think about when you write your composition.

REMEMBER—YOU SHOULD

☐ explain whether Luke's interest in clouds was just a hobby or something more.

☐ make sure each sentence you write helps the reader understand your composition.

☐ make sure you support your main point with details from the text.

☐ try to use correct spelling, capitalization, punctuation, grammar, and sentences.

4 Copyright © Pearson Education, Inc., or its affiliates. All Rights Reserved.

GO ON

Common Core State Standards

CCSS Writing 9.b. Apply grade 4 Reading standards to informational texts (e.g., "Explain how an author uses reasons and evidence to support particular points in a text"). (Also **CCSS Informational Text 1., CCSS Writing 1., CCSS Writing 4., CCSS Writing 5., CCSS Writing 9., CCSS Writing 10., CCSS Language 1., CCSS Language 2.**)

VOCABULARY

Directions

Find the word or words with the same meaning as the underlined word. Circle the letter next to the answer.

1 We wondered what was <u>rumbling</u>.

A leaving an unusual mark

B creating a flash of light

C giving off a pleasant odor

(D) making a low, rolling sound

2 Jesse looked out over the <u>lagoon</u>.

F range of snowcapped mountains

G beach covered with sand dunes

(H) shallow body of water

J hills covered with rocks

3 Steve climbed that <u>massive</u> rock.

A jagged

(B) enormous

C dangerous

D majestic

4 Some fish live in <u>tropical</u> waters.

(F) warm

G calm

H polluted

J unfamiliar

5 The birds fly over the <u>bluff</u>.

A forest

B prairie

(C) cliff

D ocean

6 My father is a <u>biologist</u> who teaches at a college.

F scientist who studies chemicals

(G) scientist who studies living things

H scientist who studies rocks

J scientist who studies stars

GO ON

> **Common Core State Standards**

Questions 1–6: CCSS Language 4. Determine or clarify the meaning of unknown and multiple-meaning words and phrases based on *grade 4 reading and content*, choosing flexibly from a range of strategies.

WORD ANALYSIS

Directions

Find the words with the same meaning as the underlined word. Circle the letter next to the answer.

7 Speak into the <u>microphone</u> clearly.

- A a tool for making phone calls
- B an instrument that produces light
- Ⓒ a device for making sounds louder
- D a machine for making copies

8 I can't believe you got her <u>autograph</u>!

- F a book
- Ⓖ a signature
- H a pen
- J a car

9 I just finished reading a <u>biography</u> of John Lennon.

- Ⓐ story of someone's life
- B story of someone's birth
- C story of someone's crimes
- D story of someone's secrets

10 Thomas Edison invented an early <u>phonograph</u>.

- F a machine for sending messages
- G a machine for recording earthquakes
- H a machine for making movies
- Ⓙ a machine for recording and playing sounds

11 I want to buy a frame for that <u>photograph</u>.

- A a device for playing records
- B science of life
- C science of the earth
- Ⓓ a picture made using a camera

12 I am taking a <u>biology</u> class next year.

- F the study of earth
- Ⓖ the study of life
- H the study of stars
- J the study of chemicals

COMPREHENSION

Bridges

People use bridges to get across places. Bridges cross over bodies of water, busy roads, and train tracks. Sometimes people build bridges between two tall buildings. This way they can cross from one to the other without going outside. A bridge can be a board of wood laid across a hole in a sidewalk. It can be steel beams running across a broad river.

If you go to Italy or Spain, you can walk on bridges that are about 2,000 years old. The Romans were good at building many kinds of things. They built stone bridges across rivers so that people would not have to swim or take a boat. The heavy stones rest on one another, holding the bridge together. Huge stone columns reach to the bottom of the river below.

GO ON

Common Core State Standards

Questions 7–12: CCSS Foundational Skills 3.a. Use combined knowledge of all letter-sound correspondences, syllabication patterns, and morphology (e.g., roots and affixes) to read accurately unfamiliar multisyllabic words in context and out of context.

Many Roman bridges are designed in the same way. They have flat surfaces that sit on top of a row of rounded arches. Millions of people use these bridges every day. These bridges are among the greatest works of the Roman Empire.

Europeans built bridges this way for more than 1,500 years. Thousands of these stone bridges still stand. From the Middle Ages onward, workers began to make bridges more beautiful. They carved patterns and pictures into them.

If you go to France, you can see one of the most beautiful bridges of all. It is the bridge of Chenonceau (sheh-non-SO) castle. This castle is built on top of the bridge; the bridge's surface is the castle's lowest floor. The building appears to float above the water on a row of arches.

Only around the year 1700 did people learn ways to build new types of bridges. New materials like iron and steel were strong. They were also comparatively easy to work with. In the 1800s and early 1900s, inventors developed trains and cars. They made it easier to travel, and more and more people were on the move. People had to make longer, stronger bridges.

A long bridge is very heavy. Workers had to find ways to support its weight. They invented the concept of the suspension bridge. It gets its name because the road is suspended, or hung, from above. A suspension bridge has a tall tower or towers. Heavy, thick cables run from the top of each tower to the ends of the bridge. The cables carry the bridge's weight.

The Brooklyn Bridge, built in 1883, is the world's most famous suspension bridge. It was the first bridge to join Brooklyn to Manhattan. The Brooklyn Bridge is one of New York's finest works of architecture.

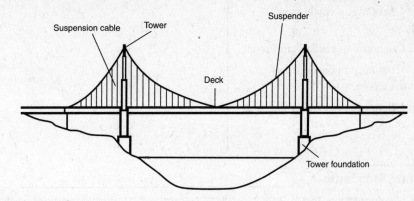

GO ON

Directions

Choose the item that best answers each question about the selection you just read. Circle the letter next to the answer.

13 Which of the following is a statement of opinion?

A   A suspension bridge has a tall tower or towers.

(B) The Brooklyn Bridge is one of New York's finest works of architecture.

C   New materials like iron and steel were strong.

D   Europeans built bridges this way for more than 1,500 years.

14 Why are modern bridges longer and stronger than older ones?

(F) They have to carry heavy trains and other traffic.

G   Builders now have lost some of the old bridge-building knowledge.

H   In old times, the builders did not know how to build strong bridges.

J   In old times, it was more important for a bridge to be beautiful.

15 According to the diagram, what do you call the area upon which cars drive?

(A) deck

B   suspension cable

C   tower

D   suspender

16 Which of the following is a statement of opinion?

F   The bridge of Chenonceau castle is in the Loire Valley.

G   The bridge of Chenonceau castle is in France.

H   The bridge of Chenonceau castle flows directly from the castle.

(J) The bridge of Chenonceau castle is the most beautiful bridge of all.

17 The purpose of a bridge is to

A   be made of stone, iron, or steel.

B   last for hundreds of years.

(C) carry people across a difficult place.

D   hang its weight from its cables.

18 "A suspension bridge has a tall tower or towers" is

(F) a statement of fact.

G   a statement of opinion.

H   neither a fact nor an opinion.

J   both a fact and an opinion.

19 Which sentence in paragraph 3 expresses an opinion?

A   the first sentence

B   the second sentence

C   the third sentence

(D) the fourth sentence

20 "The Romans were good at building many kinds of things" is

F   a statement of fact.

(G) a statement of opinion.

H   a supporting detail.

J   the article's main idea.

GO ON

Common Core State Standards

Questions 13–14, 16–20: CCSS Informational Text 1. Refer to details and examples in a text when explaining what the text says explicitly and when drawing inferences from the text. **Question 15: CCSS Informational Text 7.** Interpret information presented visually, orally, or quantitatively (e.g., in charts, graphs, diagrams, time lines, animations, or interactive elements on Web pages) and explain how the information contributes to an understanding of the text in which it appears.

WRITTEN RESPONSE TO THE SELECTION

> **Look Back and Write** Look back at pages 359–361. Do you believe
> that the whales will always be a part of Adelina's life? Why or why not?
> Provide evidence from the text to support your answer.

The information in the box below will help you remember what you should think about when you write your composition.

REMEMBER—YOU SHOULD

☐   tell why you believe or don't believe that whales will always be part of Adelina's life.

☐   use details from the text to support your ideas.

☐   organize your ideas in a logical way so that the reader understands what you are saying.

☐   try to use correct spelling, capitalization, punctuation, grammar, and sentences.

GO ON

Common Core State Standards

CCSS Writing 9.b. Apply grade 4 Reading standards to informational texts (e.g., "Explain how an author uses reasons and evidence to support particular points in a text"). (Also **CCSS Informational Text 1., CCSS Writing 1., CCSS Writing 4., CCSS Writing 5., CCSS Writing 9., CCSS Writing 10., CCSS Language 1., CCSS Language 2.)**

VOCABULARY

Directions

Find the word or words with the same meaning as the underlined word. Circle the letter next to the answer.

1 The crown <u>gleamed</u> on the queen's head.

(A) glittered

B slanted

C wobbled

D appeared

2 The water was <u>shimmering</u>.

F swirling

(G) sparkling

H foaming

J gurgling

3 She has <u>brilliant</u> eyes.

A cheerful

B charming

C ordinary

(D) shining

4 Janelle sang in the <u>chorus</u>.

F play

G movie

(H) choir

J musical

5 He is a <u>coward</u>.

(A) person who lacks courage

B person who has no talent

C person who is not honest

D person who makes bad choices

GO ON

Common Core State Standards

Questions 1–5: CCSS Language 4. Determine or clarify the meaning of unknown and multiple-meaning words and phrases based on *grade 4 reading and content,* choosing flexibly from a range of strategies.

WORD ANALYSIS

Directions
Find the word related to the underlined word. Circle the letter next to the answer.

6 When Kim saw who was going to pitch, she almost lost her <u>nerve</u>.

   F serving

   Ⓖ unnerving

   H curve

   J never

7 The <u>musicians</u> tuned their instruments before the concert.

   Ⓐ music

   B musk

   C mustard

   D muscles

8 The freshly cut flowers gave off a <u>pleasant</u> scent.

   F plaster

   G present

   Ⓗ pleasure

   J plentiful

9 There are nine <u>justices</u> on the Supreme Court.

   A rustic

   B mistrust

   C suggest

   Ⓓ unjust

10 Only the black cat's glowing eyes were <u>visible</u> in the dark room.

   Ⓕ television

   G vice

   H vibrate

   J village

11 We always eat <u>dinner</u> on the porch in warm weather.

   A dental

   Ⓑ dine

   C dinosaur

   D didn't

12 The magician was able to make a pony disappear because he <u>misdirected</u> the audience's attention.

   F misery

   G rectangle

   H dirty

   Ⓙ directions

Common Core State Standards

Questions 6–12: **CCSS Language 4.b.** Use common, grade-appropriate Greek and Latin affixes and roots as clues to the meaning of a word (e.g., *telegraph, photograph, autograph*).

COMPREHENSION

Demeter and Persephone
of Greek Mythology

Demeter was the goddess of the harvest. She watched over the fields of grain. She blessed the orchards so that the trees would bear fruit. Demeter made sure the crops got rain and sunshine.

Persephone was Demeter's only child. She was a beautiful girl. Everyone who saw her fell in love with her. While her mother went about her duties, Persephone wandered far and wide across the meadows.

One day, Hades, the god of the underworld, saw Persephone in the fields. He fell under the spell of her beauty and decided to make her his queen. But Hades was a frightening god. He was dark, harsh, and fierce. He feared that Persephone would run from him, so he quickly pulled her into his chariot and swept her away to his underground kingdom.

Persephone was unhappy in Hades's kingdom. It was always dark. It was filled with the souls of the dead. They were always grim and silent. It was nothing like the world of sunshine and air that she had left behind.

Demeter soon discovered that Persephone was missing. When she learned where her child had been taken, she went mad with sadness. She no longer cared for the grain or the fruit trees. No grapes grew on the vines. The sun refused to shine. The world grew barren and bleak. It seemed that nothing could comfort Demeter.

Other gods appealed to Hades to let Persephone go. He finally agreed that she could leave the underworld if she had eaten nothing during her stay. When Persephone heard this, she wept. She confessed that her hunger had made her eat six pomegranate seeds.

The king of the gods declared that for each seed, Persephone must remain underground for one month each year. This meant six months with Hades and six months with her mother. Demeter was so overjoyed to see her daughter again that she agreed to the bargain.

And this is why we have six months of fall and winter, every year. No crops grow, the air is cold, and there is little sun. During those six months, Demeter grieves for Persephone, lost in the kingdom of the dead. But for the six months of spring and summer, Persephone rejoins her mother. The sun shines all day long. The flowers bloom, the trees bear fruit, and the birds sing.

GO ON

Directions

Choose the item that best answers each question about the selection you just read. Circle the letter next to the answer.

13 Which statement supports the generalization "It was always dark in the underworld"?

   A Hades was a harsh, dark, and fierce man.

   B Winter and fall have longer nights than spring and summer.

   C The underworld is the kingdom of the dead.

   (D) The sun does not shine underground.

14 Demeter stopped taking care of the crops because

   F she was too busy searching for Persephone.

   (G) she was too crazy with grief over losing Persephone.

   H she was too angry with Hades to attend to her duties.

   J she lost her powers when Persephone left her.

15 Which statement from the story is a generalization?

   (A) Everyone who saw her fell in love with her.

   B Other gods appealed to Hades to let Persephone go.

   C She no longer cared for the grain or the fruit trees.

   D Persephone was Demeter's only child.

16 Which statement from paragraph 4 is *not* a generalization?

   F It was always dark.

   G It was filled with the souls of the dead.

   (H) Persephone was unhappy in Hades' kingdom.

   J They were always grim and silent.

17 Hades agreed that Persephone could leave the underworld if

   A she would never tell anyone what the underworld was like.

   B Demeter would stop tending the crops for six months of the year.

   C she continued to walk in the fields.

   (D) she hadn't eaten while she was there.

18 Which generalization does this story support?

   F Never do your duties if you're a parent.

   (G) Never wander too far away on your own.

   H Never try to plant anything in the fall or winter.

   J No one is ever happy during the fall or winter.

19 Which generalization is supported by details from the story?

   A All mothers go crazy with grief when their children leave home.

   (B) Everyone in the underworld is unhappy.

   C No one in the world is able to grow crops in warm weather.

   D All girls who wander in the fields are beautiful.

20 What natural phenomenon does this myth account for?

   F the color of fruits

   G the phases of the moon

   (H) the changing of the seasons

   J the darkness of nighttime

Common Core State Standards

Questions 13–20: CCSS Literature 1. Refer to details and examples in a text when explaining what the text says explicitly and when drawing inferences from the text.

WRITTEN RESPONSE TO THE SELECTION

> **Look Back and Write** Look back at page 390. The text explains how three things came to be. Write what they are and why they are there at the end of the night. Provide evidence to support your answer.

The information in the box below will help you remember what you should think about when you write your composition.

REMEMBER—YOU SHOULD

☐ explain what three things came to be by the end of the night and why.

☐ be sure to write about all three things.

☐ include descriptive details that appeal to one or more of the five senses.

☐ try to use correct spelling, capitalization, punctuation, grammar, and sentences.

GO ON

Common Core State Standards

CCSS Writing 9.a. Apply grade 4 Reading standards to literature (e.g., "Describe in depth a character, setting, or event in a story or drama, drawing on specific details in the text [e.g., a character's thoughts, words, or actions]."). (Also **CCSS Literature 1., CCSS Literature 2., CCSS Literature 3., CCSS Writing 4., CCSS Writing 5., CCSS Writing 10., CCSS Language 1., CCSS Language 2.**)

VOCABULARY

Directions

Find the word or words with the same meaning as the underlined word. Circle the letter next to the answer.

1 There was a **surge** toward the exit.

A fistfight

B celebration

C loud noise

D rushing motion

2 Her **forecasts** are often wrong.

F predictions

G answers

H ideas

J facts

3 The **destruction** was widespread.

A joy

B ruin

C knowledge

D power

4 My sister might **shatter** the pitcher.

F like

G paint

H break

J wash

5 That is not what I **expected**.

A thought would happen

B remembered

C feared would happen

D wanted to talk about

6 If you go **inland**, you can see the forest.

F to the east

G to the west

H toward the coast

J away from the coast

Common Core State Standards

Questions 1, 3, 5: **CCSS Language 4.b.** Use common, grade-appropriate Greek and Latin affixes and roots as clues to the meaning of a word (e.g., *telegraph, photograph, autograph*). Questions 2, 4, 6: **CCSS Foundational Skills 3.a.** Use combined knowledge of all letter-sound correspondences, syllabication patterns, and morphology (e.g., roots and affixes) to read accurately unfamiliar multisyllabic words in context and out of context.

WORD ANALYSIS

*D*irections

Find the word or words with the same meaning as the underlined word. Circle the letter next to the answer.

7 My little brother <u>scribbled</u> on my homework.

A cried loudly

B rolled over

C spoke in riddles

(D) wrote carelessly

8 Please <u>instruct</u> your brother to behave.

F allow

G force

(H) order

J change

9 It was a very big <u>construction</u> project.

(A) building

B singing

C writing

D cleaning

10 The <u>manuscript</u> was very valuable.

F oil painting

G piece of jewelry

H antique dress

(J) pages written by hand

11 That was an extremely <u>destructive</u> fire.

A long-lasting

(B) causing much damage

C fast-starting

D hard to put out

12 She <u>inscribed</u> her name on a piece of wood.

(F) carved

G sang

H wished

J wanted

COMPREHENSION

The Boston Tea Party

The date was December 16, 1773. The place was Boston Harbor. The British ship *Dartmouth* sat quietly at anchor. The night was dark and quiet. Suddenly, the still harbor came to life as a group of Indians marched to the dock. They swarmed aboard the *Dartmouth*. They broke open dozens of wooden crates of tea the ship had carried from England. They dumped the tea into the harbor. A huge crowd of friends cheered them from the docks. Why was this "tea party" taking place?

Boston was the capital of Massachusetts, one of thirteen English colonies in North America. On paper, England ruled its colonies from across the ocean. However, England let the Americans make many of their own rules. The distance was too far for England to make every little decision.

Things had begun to change by the 1760s. England began to tighten its rule over the

GO ON

Common Core State Standards

Questions 7–12: Language 4.b. Use common, grade-appropriate Greek and Latin affixes and roots as clues to the meaning of a word (e.g., *telegraph, photograph, autograph*).

Weekly Test 14 Unit 3 Week 4

Americans. The Americans reacted angrily. They were used to making their own decisions. They argued that since they had no voice in England's government, England had no right to make their laws for them.

England angered the Americans by passing several new laws, or Acts. Each Act set up a new tax on goods that America bought from England. The Townshend Acts of 1767 taxed paper, paint, glass, and tea. The Americans refused to pay the taxes. They did not buy English tea any more. Instead, they drank Dutch tea, which cost less money.

England decided to lower the price of its tea. Now, even with the tax, the English tea would cost less than the Dutch tea. England loaded the *Dartmouth* with crates of tea, and the ship arrived in Boston Harbor in November.

The dockworkers in Boston refused to unload the tea. They saw through the trick England was trying to play. However, the storeowners who had agreed to sell the tea would not let the *Dartmouth* leave the harbor. By law, they could take the tea from the ship in three weeks. They could then put it on sale.

A group of patriots met in secret. They decided not to allow this to happen. They agreed to board the ship and destroy the cargo. They would dress up like Indians so that no one would know who they were. The plan worked perfectly. To this day, no one knows exactly who took part in the Boston Tea Party.

News of the Boston Tea Party soon reached England. The government was outraged. England soon passed four new laws to punish America for the Tea Party. Americans called these new laws "the Intolerable Acts" because they were too harsh to be tolerated, or accepted.

Name of Intolerable Act	What It Said
Boston Port Act	• closed the port of Boston so that no goods could come in or go out until Boston paid for the *Dartmouth* tea
Massachusetts Government Act	• overturned the colony's Charter of Government • strengthened the rule of the governor, who was chosen by England
Administration of Justice Act	• stated that no English official could be tried for a crime in Massachusetts
Quartering Act	• forced Americans to provide housing and food for British soldiers

Directions

Choose the item that best answers each question about the selection you just read. Circle the letter next to the answer.

13 Why didn't the colonists want to pay new taxes?

A because they were too poor to pay more taxes

B because they wanted to go to war with England

Ⓒ because they did not have a voice in the English government

D because they never used the taxed paper, paint, glass, or tea

14 Which sentence states an effect of the Townshend Acts of 1767?

F Americans bought more English tea.

Ⓖ Americans stopped buying English tea.

H American stopped buying Dutch tea.

J Americans stopped drinking tea.

15 Why did the English lower the price of their tea?

Ⓐ because they wanted Americans to buy the tea

B because they wanted Americans to produce their own tea

C because they wanted to trick Americans into drinking coffee

D because they wanted the Dutch to lower the price of their tea

16 Which group of people did not want to unload the cargo of tea from the *Dartmouth*?

F officials of the English government

Ⓖ Boston dockworkers

H American Indians from the area

J Boston storeowners

17 Why did the English pass "the Intolerable Acts"?

A because they wanted to improve trade with the colonies

B because they wanted to improve trade with the Dutch

C because they wanted to reward America for the Boston Tea Party

Ⓓ because they wanted to punish America for the Boston Tea Party

18 What was an effect of the Massachusetts Government Act?

F It strengthened the colony's government.

G It gave Americans more freedom.

Ⓗ It increased England's rule over the colony.

J It improved trade between England and America.

19 According to the Boston Port Act, the port of Boston would be closed until

Ⓐ the tea was paid for.

B the governor was chosen.

C the patriots apologized.

D the British soldiers arrived.

20 Read paragraph 7. You can conclude that the people who dumped the tea were

Ⓕ very loyal to one another.

G very violent and destructive.

H not very good at making plans.

J not very clever or smart.

GO ON

Common Core State Standards

Questions 13–18, 20: CCSS Informational Text 3. Explain events, procedures, ideas, or concepts in a historical, scientific, or technical text, including what happened and why, based on specific information in the text. **Question 19: CCSS Informational Text 7.** Interpret information presented visually, orally, or quantitatively (e.g., in charts, graphs, diagrams, time lines, animations, or interactive elements on Web pages) and explain how the information contributes to an understanding of the text in which it appears.

WRITTEN RESPONSE TO THE SELECTION

> **Look Back and Write** Look back at page 413. Why does Warren Faidley need a safe place to stay when he photographs a hurricane? What does he look for in a shelter? Provide evidence to support your answer.

The information in the box below will help you remember what you should think about when you write your composition.

REMEMBER—YOU SHOULD

☐ write about why Warren Faidley needs a safe place to photograph hurricanes and what he looks for in a shelter.

☐ be sure your response answers both questions.

☐ be sure to state good reasons for the choices Faidley makes.

☐ try to use correct spelling, capitalization, punctuation, grammar, and sentences.

GO ON

Common Core State Standards

CCSS Writing 9.b. Apply grade 4 Reading standards to informational texts (e.g., "Explain how an author uses reasons and evidence to support particular points in a text"). (Also **CCSS Informational Text 1., CCSS Informational Text 3., CCSS Writing 2., CCSS Writing 4., CCSS Writing 5., CCSS Writing 10., CCSS Language 1., CCSS Language 2.**)

VOCABULARY

Directions

Find the word or words with the same meaning as the underlined word. Circle the letter next to the answer.

1 The <u>lumberjacks</u> ate a big breakfast.

(A) people who work with trees

B people who work with animals

C people who work outdoors

D people who work at night

2 You can post the <u>announcement</u> on the board.

F junk mail

G friendly letter

(H) public notice

J private message

3 Tomorrow the snow will <u>thaw</u>.

A fall heavily

(B) start to melt

C blow about

D freeze solid

4 Be careful around <u>untamed</u> animals.

F dangerous

G large

(H) wild

J gentle

5 Here is a list of the main <u>requirements</u>.

(A) things needed

B things purchased

C things stolen

D things left over

6 The horse's <u>harness</u> was expensive.

F food made from oats and hay

G pieces of metal nailed to an animal's hooves

H seat used by a person riding a horse

(J) straps linking an animal to a cart or plow

7 Muffins are a special <u>feature</u> at this bakery.

(A) thing that stands out

B thing that tastes good

C thing that costs very little

D thing that is unnatural

Common Core State Standards

Questions 2, 4–5: CCSS Language 4.b. Use common, grade-appropriate Greek and Latin affixes and roots as clues to the meaning of a word (e.g., *telegraph, photograph, autograph*). **Questions 1, 3, 6–7: CCSS Language 4.** Determine or clarify the meaning of unknown and multiple-meaning words and phrases based on *grade 4 reading and content,* choosing flexibly from a range of strategies.

WORD ANALYSIS

Directions
Find the word related to the underlined word. Circle the letter next to the answer.

8 She was a famous opera <u>singer</u>.

   F wringer

   G spring

   H sting

   Ⓙ song

9 That train will <u>depart</u> from Track 12.

   Ⓐ parting

   B depress

   C repair

   D depend

10 That paragraph is a <u>digression</u>.

   F digit

   Ⓖ progress

   H restive

   J illusion

11 That <u>structure</u> may fall over in a high wind.

   A strum

   Ⓑ destruction

   C consume

   D capture

12 Please <u>choose</u> the one you like best.

   F chop

   G change

   Ⓗ choice

   J cheat

Common Core State Standards

Questions 8–12: CCSS Language 5.c. Demonstrate understanding of words by relating them to their opposites (antonyms) and to words with similar but not identical meanings (synonyms).

COMPREHENSION

Paul Bunyan

Paul Bunyan was the most famous lumberjack ever to split a rail. His laugh was so loud that people heard it miles away and thought it was a thunderstorm. When Paul got angry, his eyes flashed sparks that lit up the sky. That was the lightning.

Babe the Blue Ox was Paul's best friend. Babe stood out among the other oxen because he was as blue as the ocean. He was bigger than any other ox in the West. When Babe pawed up the ground to find food, he created the Grand Canyon. He could haul an entire forest of logs to camp in one day's work.

One day a train broke down on the tracks. There were hundreds of cars in the train. It was easy for Paul and Babe to help. Paul just harnessed Babe to the engine and then yelled "Git up!" Babe lowered his head and started forward. His mighty shoulders pulled the engine forward. Soon the cars of the train were back in line. The passengers waved out the windows to Babe and Paul as the train went by.

Paul Bunyan could eat enough for twelve men! Every morning, the cook scrambled two dozen eggs. She fried two pounds of bacon and made a gallon of hot, black coffee. Paul finished it all in the wink of an eye.

One time, the boss hired Paul to dig a deep well. Paul dug faster than any man alive. He tossed up tons of dirt behind him as he worked. Before he knew it, he was peeking clear through to the other side of the Earth. The mounds of dirt he dug up are now called the Rocky Mountains.

The cook liked to tell the story of Paul's garden. Paul could grow vegetables in any kind of soil. One year he grew so many peas that the cook told him she could never shell them all. Paul Bunyan had a bright idea. He called for all the other lumberjacks and their girls to come over. Everyone danced to the music of the fiddle and flute. Paul had spread the pea pods all over the floor. The dancer's feet made the pods pop open. By the time the party ended, all the peas were shelled!

The boss called Paul and Babe in to help when the Alaskan Pipeline froze solid. Paul breathed on the outside of the pipe. His breath was so hot that it melted through the ice right away. Soon the oil was flowing through the pipe again.

GO ON

Directions

Choose the item that best answers each question about the selection you just read. Circle the letter next to the answer.

13 What happened when Paul Bunyan dug a well?

(A) He created the Rocky Mountains.

B He created the Grand Canyon.

C He built the Alaskan Pipeline.

D He made a huge vegetable garden.

14 What generalization about lumberjacks does this story support?

(F) They are strong.

G They are able to dance.

H They are good gardeners.

J They eat a lot of eggs and bacon.

15 Read paragraph 6. Which statement is a generalization?

A The cook liked to tell the story of Paul's garden.

(B) Paul could grow vegetables in any kind of soil.

C Paul Bunyan had a bright idea.

D The dancer's feet made the pods pop open.

16 Based on his actions, you can conclude that Paul Bunyan was

F gentle and quiet.

G angry and violent.

H strong and sad.

(J) friendly and helpful.

17 What generalization can you make about oxen based on this story?

A They do not like to be around people.

B They have huge appetites for food.

C They are usually blue in color.

(D) They are very strong.

18 Which detail shows that this story is a tall tale?

F Babe was a strong ox.

G One day a train broke down on the tracks.

(H) Paul's breath melted all the ice right away.

J The boss hired Paul to dig a deep well.

19 Which generalization might you make about many of the details of this story?

A They provide a realistic view of life in the Old West.

(B) They are exaggerated for the sake of humor.

C They make the story dull and lifeless.

D They prove that Paul Bunyan was a real person.

20 Based on this story, which generalization is *not* true of most tall tales?

F They are full of colorful, improbable details.

G They feature people who are larger than life.

H They are entertaining and funny.

(J) They tell about real people from history.

GO ON

Common Core State Standards

Questions 13–20: CCSS Literature 1. Refer to details and examples in a text when explaining what the text says explicitly and when drawing inferences from the text.

WRITTEN RESPONSE TO THE SELECTION

Look Back and Write Look back at the question on page 437. How does this tall tale explain changes in nature? Provide evidence to support your answer.

The information in the box below will help you remember what you should think about when you write your composition.

REMEMBER—YOU SHOULD

☐ write about how the story explains changes in the natural world.

☐ begin with a sentence that will grab the reader's attention.

☐ use precise and imaginative words to describe the changes and how they came about.

☐ try to use correct spelling, capitalization, punctuation, grammar, and sentences.

Common Core State Standards

CCSS Writing 9.a. Apply grade 4 Reading standards to literature (e.g., "Describe in depth a character, setting, or event in a story or drama, drawing on specific details in the text [e.g., a character's thoughts, words, or actions].")." (Also **CCSS Literature 1.**, **CCSS Literature 2., CCSS Writing 4., CCSS Writing 5., CCSS Writing 10., CCSS Language 1., CCSS Language 2.**)

_____

_____

_____

_____

_____

_____

_____

_____

_____

_____

_____

_____

_____

_____

_____

_____

_____

_____

_____

_____

VOCABULARY

Directions

Find the word or words with the same meaning as the underlined word. Circle the letter next to the answer.

1 Do you know the <u>identity</u> of that animal?

A call

B name

C heal

D lecture

2 That dog is a <u>relentless</u> barker.

F nonstop

G strong

H weak

J loud

3 Did you read his <u>analysis</u> of the experiment?

A short report

B quick sketch

C detailed examination

D exact record

4 Look at the cells in the <u>microscope</u>.

F device that keep things alive

G device that freezes things

H device that makes things look smaller

J device that makes things look larger

5 The recipe calls for a <u>precise</u> amount of lemon juice.

A small

B large

C exact

D varied

6 The raccoon lives in a <u>hollow</u> log.

F empty

G dry

H long

J round

7 Fill the <u>beakers</u> with water.

A containers used for cleaning

B containers used in laboratories

C containers used for dogs

D containers used for cooking

GO ON

Common Core State Standards

Questions 1–7: CCSS Language 4.a. Use context (e.g., definitions, examples, or restatements in text) as a clue to the meaning of a word or phrase.

WORD ANALYSIS

Directions

Find the words with the same meaning as the underlined word. Circle the letter next to the answer.

8 After the banquet, a talented <u>magician</u> entertained us.

F person who recites poetry

(G) person skilled in stage magic

H person who studies how magnets work

J person who draws funny portraits

9 The <u>pianist</u> took a bow.

(A) person who plays the piano

B person who tunes pianos

C person who makes pianos

D person who listens to piano music

10 She was an experienced <u>naturalist</u>.

F person who creates art on walls

G person who organizes things

H person who seems to know everything

(J) person who studies nature

11 Benjamin Franklin was a famous <u>Pennsylvanian</u>.

A a person who admires Pennsylvania

B a person who has never been to Pennsylvania

(C) a person from Pennsylvania

D a person who hates Pennsylvania

12 Frances's <u>idealism</u> helps her resist all temptations that come her way.

(F) having high ideals

G having original ideas

H unusual appearance

J exact resemblance to another person

COMPREHENSION

Marian Anderson at the Lincoln Memorial

It was a bright, cold day in March. Suzie dragged her feet as we marched along the crooked sidewalks to my music lesson. She was my best friend, and we had always done everything together, ever since we were little babies. But Suzie didn't care about singing. She just came along to be with me. I wanted to be a great singer like Miss Marian Anderson.

We were lucky to live in Washington, D.C. Miss Lauder was a great music teacher. She sometimes got free tickets to concerts. Suzie and I could not always go with her to

GO ON

GO ON

Common Core State Standards

Questions 8–12: CCSS Language 4.b. Use common, grade-appropriate Greek and Latin affixes and roots as clues to the meaning of a word (e.g., *telegraph, photograph, autograph*).

the concerts because some of the concert halls didn't let colored people in. But lots of the concerts were in churches, and anyone could go into a church.

Suzie and I always raced down the last block. She always won. We were giggling as we tumbled up the porch steps and pushed the bell. Miss Lauder let us in. I could see she was excited about something. She told us about it as we hung up our coats.

Miss Marian Anderson was supposed to sing at Constitution Hall. But the people who owned the Hall said it was "whites only." No colored person could perform there. Suzie and I stared at each other. Miss Anderson was famous all over the world. How could people not want her to sing?

Miss Lauder told us there was still hope. She said that many important people were fighting for Miss Anderson. She told us that Mrs. Franklin D. Roosevelt, the President's wife, had written a letter telling the owners of the Hall that they were wrong. She showed us the letter in the paper. Mrs. Roosevelt called Miss Anderson "a great artist" and said that the owners of Constitution Hall had failed.

Suzie and I got excited. Eleanor Roosevelt was the First Lady of the United States. Somebody so important must be able to help Miss Anderson!

There were a lot of angry people in Washington that month. Every day Suzie and I heard something about Miss Anderson on the radio. We both thought it was really important that she be allowed to sing. In the end, we heard that she would sing at the Lincoln Memorial. Anyone could go to the concert. My parents talked about it over dinner. They promised we would go to hear Miss Anderson sing.

The concert was on Easter Sunday. After church, we went to the Memorial. Suzie came too. I'd never seen so many people in one place; there must have been thousands of them. Everybody was all dressed up, serious, and polite. It was cold for April. I huddled in my coat.

Miss Marian Anderson walked out from inside the Lincoln Memorial. She stood on the steps in her beautiful fur coat. A man introduced her. My papa said he was someone important from the White House. Then Miss Anderson opened her mouth and began to sing.

Directions

Choose the item that best answers each question about the selection you just read. Circle the letter next to the answer.

13 How is Suzie different from the narrator?

(A) Suzie doesn't care to learn to sing.

B Suzie can't run as fast.

C Suzie doesn't like to go to concerts.

D Suzie isn't interested in Marian Anderson.

14 What do Marian Anderson and Miss Lauder have in common?

F They are both African-American.

(G) They both love music.

H They are both famous.

J They are both real people from history.

15 How is the narrator like Marian Anderson?

A They both live in Washington, D.C.

B They're both friends with Eleanor Roosevelt.

C They're both famous all over the world.

(D) They both enjoy singing.

16 What caused Marian Anderson to sing at the Lincoln Memorial?

(F) The owners of Constitution Hall said it was for "whites only."

G Eleanor Roosevelt wrote a letter asking her to sing there.

H A larger audience could hear her if she sang outdoors.

J She wanted to honor the memory of Abraham Lincoln.

17 Why does everyone think Mrs. Roosevelt can help Marian Anderson?

(A) Mrs. Roosevelt is the President's wife.

B Mrs. Roosevelt loves music.

C Mrs. Roosevelt is African-American.

D Mrs. Roosevelt is a real person from history.

18 Mrs. Roosevelt and Miss Lauder are alike because

F they are married to presidents.

G they write letters to newspapers.

(H) they want to help Marian Anderson.

J they are musicians.

19 How are Suzie and the narrator alike?

A They both run fast.

B They both go to church before the concert.

(C) They both live in Washington, D.C.

D They are both good students at school.

20 Which is the best description of Mrs. Roosevelt's character?

(F) kind and fair

G angry and rude

H thoughtful and quiet

J funny and smart

 GO ON

Common Core State Standards

Questions 13–20: CCSS Literature 1. Refer to details and examples in a text when explaining what the text says explicitly and when drawing inferences from the text.

WRITTEN RESPONSE TO THE SELECTION

> **Look Back and Write** Look back at pages 39–40. Why do you think Drake and Nell are successful as a team of science detectives? Provide evidence to support your answer.

The information in the box below will help you remember what you should think about when you write your composition.

REMEMBER—YOU SHOULD

☐ explain why Drake and Nell are a successful team of science detectives.

☐ begin your response with a sentence that states your main idea, or central thought, in an interesting way.

☐ include as many facts or examples as you can to support your opinion.

☐ try to use correct spelling, capitalization, punctuation, grammar, and sentences.

GO ON

Common Core State Standards

CCSS Writing 1. Write opinion pieces on topics or texts, supporting a point of view with reasons and information. (Also **CCSS Literature 1.**, **CCSS Literature 3.**, **CCSS Writing 4.**, **CCSS Writing 5.**, **CCSS Writing 9.**, **CCSS Writing 9.a.**, **CCSS Writing 10.**, **CCSS Language 1.**, **CCSS Language 2.**)

_____

_____

_____

_____

_____

_____

_____

_____

_____

_____

_____

_____

_____

_____

_____

_____

_____

_____

_____

_____

VOCABULARY

Directions

Find the word or words with the same meaning as the underlined word. Circle the letter next to the answer.

1 We saw the <u>enchanted</u> sea.

A polluted

B imaginary

C peaceful

(D) magical

2 The students watched the <u>dolphins</u>.

(F) marine mammals

G flying insects

H fresh-water fish

J desert reptiles

3 My cat purrs with rumbling <u>pulses</u>.

A deep breaths

B heavy sighs

(C) rhythmic beats

D excited meows

4 I need <u>flexible</u> material.

F comfortable

(G) stretchable

H washable

J remarkable

5 She reached the <u>surface</u>.

(A) outer edge

B far side

C highest peak

D exact center

6 Jake bought a new <u>aquarium</u>.

F birdcage

(G) fish tank

H doghouse

J horse barn

7 We caught only a few <u>glimpses</u>.

A photographs

B short stories

C complaints

(D) brief views

Common Core State Standards

Questions 1–7: CCSS Language 4. Determine or clarify the meaning of unknown and multiple-meaning words and phrases based on *grade 4 reading and content,* choosing flexibly from a range of strategies.

WORD ANALYSIS

Directions
Find the words with the same meaning as the underlined word. Circle the letter next to the answer.

8 Those fish are <u>aquatic</u> creatures.

(F) of the water
G of the south
H of the tropics
J of the past

9 It was hard to <u>predict</u> the ending.

A to look before
(B) to state before
C to lead before
D to feel before

10 His <u>diction</u> made me think he was originally from another country.

(F) style of speaking
G facial appearance
H style of dressing
J family name

11 The Roman <u>aqueduct</u> is still standing.

A military headquarters
B court of criminal law
C temple in honor of a god
(D) bridge that carries water

12 He <u>dictated</u> his story to the recorder.

F shouted with alarm
G whistled comically
H sang prettily
(J) spoke aloud

COMPREHENSION

Cats

A house cat sees a sparrow in the garden. Her body stiffens. Her ears stand up at attention. She does not move a whisker. Her eyes stare. Then, just like a cat in the wild, she attacks!

GO ON

Common Core State Standards

Questions 8–12: CCSS Language 4.b. Use common, grade-appropriate Greek and Latin affixes and roots as clues to the meaning of a word (e.g., *telegraph, photograph, autograph*).

Your pet cat looks just like the wild cats you see on television or at the zoo. That's because they are all related to each other. Wild cats and house cats have the same shape of face and body. They have big ears that stand up and big eyes that see well in low light. They have long tails. Their paws are large and strong. The only major difference is that house cats are much smaller. Tigers and lions weigh hundreds of pounds, but most pet cats weigh only twelve pounds or less. No one quite knows how the very small cats developed from their larger cousins.

Not only do pet cats and wild cats look alike, but they also act alike. Both are great hunters. Even though a pet cat doesn't have to hunt for food as a wild cat does, it still has the skills. They practice their skills by pouncing on small toys in play. They also catch mice and chase insects that get into the house.

Cats' claws are great hunting tools. When a cat is hunting, it tightens the muscles in its paws. The sharp claws appear. When the cat relaxes, the claws retract, or pull back, into the soft paw. When house cats play with their human owners, they never use their claws unless the play gets too rough. Then they will show their claws in self-defense.

Many people are amazed at the way all cats can jump. A house cat can jump more than five times its own height! This is why you have to watch your cat very carefully if you let it outdoors. It can jump over most fences and walk along narrow ridges without losing its balance.

House cats can be divided into different groups. They can have long or short fur. They can be purebred or mixed. And they come in only a few colors. They can be black, gray, orange, tan, white, or combinations of these. The tabby pattern of black and tan stripes is the most common. Most tabbies have stripes that form the letter M on their foreheads. Black, orange, and white cats are called calico. Orange cats are known as marmalades. Black and orange cats are called tortoiseshell. There are some special kinds of house cats too. Cats called Orientals have been bred to have flat faces. The Manx cat has only a short stump of a tail. The Sphinx cat has no fur at all.

Directions

Choose the item that best answers each question about the selection you just read. Circle the letter next to the answer.

13 What is the biggest contrast between wild cats and house cats?

   A their face and body shape

   B their eyes and ears

   C their tails and paws

   (D) their size and weight

14 In what way can you compare Oriental, Manx, and Sphinx cats?

   F They can be divided into groups.

   G They have flat faces and short stumpy tails.

   (H) They are special kinds of house cats.

   J They have short fur or no fur at all.

15 Which statement is a generalization?

   (A) All cats look and act alike.

   B A cat can jump more than five times its height.

   C House cats chase mice.

   D The Sphinx cat has no fur.

16 How does the author contrast calico, marmalade, and tortoiseshell cats?

   F by whether they live indoors or outdoors

   (G) by their colors

   H by whether they have claws or not

   J by whether they are purebred or mixed

17 According to the passage, you should watch your cat when it is outdoors because

   A it may need your protection and help.

   B it can get into fights with other cats.

   C it may dig up the plants.

   (D) it can jump a high fence and run away.

18 How does the Sphinx contrast with the other cats?

   F It has a flat face.

   G It is orange.

   H It has a short tail.

   (J) It has no fur.

19 How similar are the actions of wild cats and pet cats?

   A not at all similar

   B a little bit similar

   C somewhat similar

   (D) very similar

20 Why do cats like to pounce on toys in play?

   F They are playful animals.

   G They like to exercise.

   (H) They're practicing their hunting skills.

   J They get bored easily.

GO ON

Common Core State Standards

Questions 13–14, 16, 18–19: CCSS Informational Text 5. Describe the overall structure (e.g., chronology, comparison, cause/effect, problem/solution) of events, ideas, concepts, or information in a text or part of a text. **Questions 15, 17, 20: CCSS Informational Text 1.** Refer to details and examples in a text when explaining what the text says explicitly and when drawing inferences from the text.

WRITTEN RESPONSE TO THE SELECTION

> **Look Back and Write** Look back at pages 62–63. Explain why pink dolphins are called *encantado*, or "enchanted." Provide evidence to support your answer.

The information in the box below will help you remember what you should think about when you write your composition.

REMEMBER—YOU SHOULD

☐ tell why pink dolphins in the rain forests are called *encantado*, or "enchanted."

☐ include the definition of *enchanted* that fits the word's usage in the text.

☐ support your opinion with facts and examples from the text.

☐ try to use correct spelling, capitalization, punctuation, grammar, and sentences.

Common Core State Standards

CCSS Informational Text 1. Refer to details and examples in a text when explaining what the text says explicitly and when drawing inferences from the text. (Also **CCSS Writing 2., CCSS Writing 4., CCSS Writing 5., CCSS Language 1., CCSS Language 2.**)

Name _____

VOCABULARY

Directions

Find the word or words with the same meaning as the underlined word. Circle the letter next to the answer.

1 I found several <u>messages</u> on the table.

(A) notes of information

B statements of fact

C sweet things to eat

D official forms to fill out

2 My little sister's behavior was <u>exhausting</u> me.

F making sad

G making happy

H making angry

(J) making tired

3 I would never <u>reveal</u> what I was told.

A make up

(B) make known

C understand

D cover up

4 It was <u>impossible</u> to open the door.

F rarely possible

(G) not possible

H easily possible

J sometimes possible

5 We toured the old <u>headquarters</u>.

A playrooms

B book rooms

(C) central offices

D doctor's offices

6 The <u>advance</u> guard marched along.

(F) first in order

G last in order

H highest in rank

J lowest in rank

7 He <u>developed</u> the photographs.

A labeled and filed

B framed and hung

(C) brought into being

D liked intensely

GO ON

Common Core State Standards

Questions 1–7: CCSS Language 4. Determine or clarify the meaning of unknown and multiple-meaning words and phrases based on *grade 4 reading and content,* choosing flexibly from a range of strategies.

- -

WORD ANALYSIS

*D*irections

Find the word in which the beginning *im-* or *in-* means the same as it does in the underlined word. Circle the letter next to the answer.

8 The angry man was <u>impolite</u> to the waiter.

   F   imagine

   G   imitate

  (H) imperfect

   J   import

9 I would not rely on her <u>inexpert</u> advice.

  (A) inexact

   B   inform

   C   infect

   D   inhabit

10 The air is <u>invisible</u>.

   F   insect

   G   instant

   H   inside

  (J) insecure

11 The <u>impatient</u> dog wanted its food first.

   A   immense

  (B) impure

   C   imprison

   D   imprint

12 All the test answers were <u>incorrect</u>.

  (F) indefinite

   G   inch

   H   index

   J   increase

COMPREHENSION

Tomatoes!

Many people love tomatoes. You can see them in crates in every market. In the United States, we can buy tomatoes all year round. They grow outdoors in hot weather. In the winter, people grow them indoors. People eat tomatoes at every meal of the day.

Tomatoes grow from seeds. A tomato seed is tiny and has a pale yellow color. When you cut a tomato open, you see dozens of seeds inside it. Sometimes a tomato goes bad before you can eat it. You can toss those spoiled tomatoes out into the garden. They will grow into healthy plants.

GO ON

| Common Core State Standards |

Questions 8–12: Foundational Skills 3.a. Use combined knowledge of all letter-sound correspondences, syllabication patterns, and morphology (e.g., roots and affixes) to read accurately unfamiliar multisyllabic words in context and out of context.

You can throw tomato scraps out at any time of year. If you have rich, loose soil in your garden, nature will do the planting for you. Any part of your garden that gets plenty of sunlight will be a good place for tomato plants.

In late summer, you will begin to see the plants. Tomatoes grow on vines. These long vines like to climb fences or poles. Some people build wire cages for tomatoes to climb. The vines grasp the wires and grow up the sides of the cage. If your tomato vines have nothing to climb, they will grow along the ground.

The vines and leaves are bright green. They grow very fast! Soon you will see tiny yellow flowers, shaped like little stars. After the flowers appear, you will start to see the tomatoes. They will be pale green at first. They will turn a bright, warm red as they ripen. This means they are ready to pick. If you happen to pick any that are still orange, and not yet bright red, don't worry. You can leave them on the kitchen counter for a few days and watch them change color. Like most fruits, tomatoes continue to ripen after you pick them.

When you go to the garden to pick tomatoes, always look on the ground under the plants. Ripe tomatoes can fall off the vines all by themselves. Sometimes they smash when they fall. Often, though, they are just as perfect as the tomatoes still on the vine. All you have to do is rinse the dirt off.

The vines will produce tomatoes throughout the summer and fall. The plants will die on the first night that the temperature freezes and there is frost on the ground. But most likely they will reseed themselves. You will have more plants next year!

The chart below shows you some different kinds of tomatoes and their names. The smaller a tomato is, the more flavor it has.

Name	Shape	Size
beefsteak tomato	between round and oval	about as big as two fists
tomato	round	about as big as a fist
plum tomato	oval	about as big as a plum
cherry tomato	round	as small as a green pea to as big as a cherry
grape tomato	oval	about as big as a green grape

Tomatoes can be served at any meal. A slice of a large tomato is perfect for many kinds of sandwiches. You can toss a handful of cherry or grape tomatoes into a salad or cut them up into an omelet. If you peel and crush plum tomatoes, you get a delicious sauce for pasta or pizza. Some people even have recipes that call for green tomatoes! Cooked in sugar, they taste just like apples.

GO ON

Directions

Choose the item that best answers each question about the selection you just read. Circle the letter next to the answer.

13 After a tomato plant produces tiny yellow flowers,

    A you can start picking tomatoes.

    B you can toss spoiled tomatoes into the garden.

    (C) you will start to see pale green tomatoes.

    D you will start to see bright red tomatoes.

14 Look at the chart. Which kind of tomato is the largest?

    (F) beefsteak

    G plum

    H cherry

    J grape

15 What happens to tomato vines right after the first frost of the year?

    A They put out leaves.

    B They begin to climb.

    C They begin to flower.

    (D) They die.

16 Which of the following has to happen first?

    F The vine produces tiny yellow flowers.

    (G) The vine produces green leaves.

    H The tomatoes begin to turn bright red.

    J The tomatoes are peeled and crushed for sauce.

17 Reread paragraph 3. Which generalization does the paragraph support?

    A Tomatoes need a lot of water.

    B Tomatoes are difficult to grow.

    (C) Tomatoes are easy to plant.

    D Tomatoes grow everywhere.

18 Which step should you take first if you want to grow tomatoes?

    F Learn to cook with them.

    (G) Make sure you can provide them with enough sunlight.

    H Toss spoiled tomatoes into the garden.

    J Pick the tomatoes after they turn bright red.

19 At what point would a gardener build a wire cage for a tomato plant?

    (A) right after the plant first appears and begins to grow

    B right after the plant first produces flowers

    C right after the plant first produces green tomatoes

    D right after the tomatoes start to turn red

20 According to the author, which tomato is likely to taste the best?

    F a large tomato

    G a green tomato

    H a bright red tomato

    (J) a small tomato

GO ON

Common Core State Standards

Questions 13, 15–20: CCSS Informational Text 3. Explain events, procedures, ideas, or concepts in a historical, scientific, or technical text, including what happened and why, based on specific information in the text. **Question 14: CCSS Informational Text 7.** Interpret information presented visually, orally, or quantitatively (e.g., in charts, graphs, diagrams, time lines, animations, or interactive elements on Web pages) and explain how the information contributes to an understanding of the text in which it appears.

Name _____

WRITTEN RESPONSE TO THE SELECTION

> **Look Back and Write** Look back at pages 100–101. How would you describe the character of the Navajo code talkers during World War II? Provide evidence to support your answer.

The information in the box below will help you remember what you should think about when you write your composition.

REMEMBER—YOU SHOULD

☐ describe the character of the Navajo code talkers during World War II.

☐ write a beginning sentence that clearly states your main idea.

☐ use specific details from the text to show the reader exactly what you mean.

☐ try to use correct spelling, capitalization, punctuation, grammar, and sentences.

GO ON

Common Core State Standards

CCSS Writing 9.b. Apply grade 4 Reading standards to informational texts (e.g., "Explain how an author uses reasons and evidence to support particular points in a text"). (Also **CCSS Informational Text 1., CCSS Informational Text 2., CCSS Writing 4., CCSS Writing 5., CCSS Writing 9., CCSS Writing 10., CCSS Language 1., CCSS Language 2.**)

VOCABULARY

Directions
Find the word or words with the same meaning as the underlined word. Circle the letter next to the answer.

1 The new <u>scholars</u> ate dinner.
- (A) students
- B engineers
- C assistants
- D athletes

2 This vase is <u>ancient</u>.
- F damaged
- G crystal
- (H) antique
- J brittle

3 She is a <u>seeker</u> of truth.
- A person who teaches
- (B) person who searches
- C person who writes
- D person who studies

4 Have you seen the <u>temple</u>?
- F court built for legal cases
- G theater created for concerts
- (H) building constructed to honor a god
- J arena made for sporting events

5 We found a <u>link</u>!
- (A) thing that connects
- B thing that operates
- C thing that drains
- D thing that protects

6 Lena experienced a moment of <u>triumph</u>.
- F loneliness
- G horror
- H peace
- (J) success

7 Ronnie will <u>uncover</u> the facts.
- A ignore
- (B) show
- C bury
- D study

GO ON

Common Core State Standards

Questions 1–4, 6–7: CCSS Language 4.b. Use common, grade-appropriate Greek and Latin affixes and roots as clues to the meaning of a word (e.g., *telegraph, photograph, autograph*). **Question 5: CCSS Language 4.** Determine or clarify the meaning of unknown and multiple-meaning words and phrases based on *grade 4 reading and content,* choosing flexibly from a range of strategies.

WORD ANALYSIS

Directions

Find the words with the same meaning as the underlined word. Circle the letter next to the answer.

8 Dave's dad <u>telecommuted</u> to work today.

   F worked in an office

   (G) worked far away from an office

   H worked to build an office

   J worked at a new office

9 The witch <u>transformed</u> the prince into a frog.

   A destroyed the shape of

   B colored the shape of

   (C) changed the shape of

   D improved the shape of

10 Use the <u>telephoto</u> lens for this shot.

   (F) that which makes a faraway object seem close

   G that which makes a faraway object seem farther away

   H that which makes a nearby object seem far away

   J that which makes a nearby object seem nearer

11 Charles Lindbergh is famous for the first solo <u>transatlantic</u> flight.

   A around the Atlantic Ocean

   B under the Atlantic Ocean

   (C) across the Atlantic Ocean

   D through the Atlantic Ocean

12 My mother and I <u>transplanted</u> the cherry tree.

   F planted, watered, and cared for

   G planted in a private garden

   H planted under a glass roof

   (J) moved and planted in a different place

COMPREHENSION

Satchmo!

Louis Armstrong (c. 1900–1971) was one of the greatest trumpet players in America. Many people think of his name right away when they hear the word *jazz*.

Louis was born in New Orleans. He lived with his mother and sister. Louis and his friends had a wonderful time in the city. They ran after the street musicians, listening to their music. New Orleans musicians were the best in the country. They played the blues, ragtime, and marches. Louis always listened to the trumpets. He knew he wanted to learn to play the trumpet one day.

GO ON

Common Core State Standards

Questions 8–12: Language 4.b. Use common, grade-appropriate Greek and Latin affixes and roots as clues to the meaning of a word (e.g., *telegraph, photograph, autograph*).

Name _____

When Louis was thirteen, he and his friends got into trouble with the police. Louis was sent to reform school. He was lonesome at first, but soon things got better. Louis joined the school band. He began on drums. Soon after, his wish came true. He learned to play the bugle and then the trumpet.

The school band played many concerts outside. People began to know Louis when they saw him. They cheered for his soaring high notes. Louis was becoming a real musician.

Once he left school, Louis had to work to help his mother. He had two jobs, but he still found time to practice his trumpet. He also learned to sing. As Louis grew older, his voice became famous. It was deep and sounded as if his throat were full of gravel.

In 1918 Louis joined Kid Ory's famous band. With Louis playing trumpet, the popular band had greater success than ever before. Four years later, Louis finally left New Orleans. He joined a band in Chicago. He was on his way! People found a new nickname for him— "Satchmo."

Louis had a great career in jazz. He wrote many of his own tunes. He didn't just play trumpet, but he sang as well. He traveled all over the world spreading the joy of jazz music. Louis even appeared in Hollywood films, such as *Hello, Dolly!* and *High Society*.

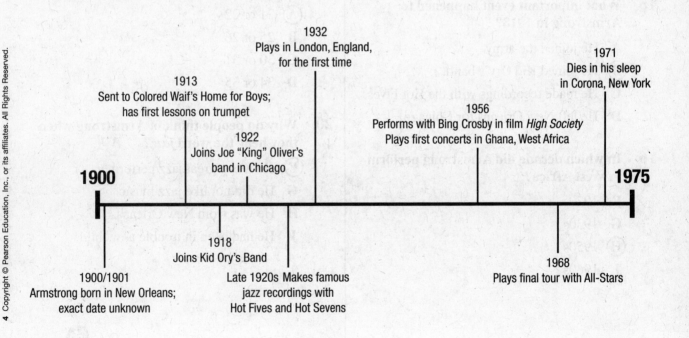

GO ON

Directions

Choose the item that best answers each question about the selection you just read. Circle the letter next to the answer.

13 What information does the time line provide?

   A the names of Armstrong's family members

   B titles of the songs Armstrong wrote

   C important events in American history

   Ⓓ important dates in Armstrong's life

14 What is the main idea of this biography?

   Ⓕ Louis Armstrong was a famous American musician.

   G Louis Armstrong went to reform school when he was young.

   H Louis Armstrong played the trumpet.

   J Louis Armstrong was born in New Orleans.

15 What important event happened to Armstrong in 1918?

   A He joined the army.

   Ⓑ He joined Kid Ory's band.

   C He made recordings with the Hot Fives.

   D He left New Orleans for Chicago.

16 In which decade did Armstrong perform in West Africa?

   F 1920s

   G 1930s

   Ⓗ 1950s

   J 1960s

17 How was Kid Ory's band different after Louis joined it?

   A The band got less and less work.

   B The band finally became famous.

   C The band members fought more often.

   Ⓓ The band was even more successful than it had been.

18 Who appeared with Armstrong in the film *High Society*?

   F Kid Ory

   Ⓖ Bing Crosby

   H Joe Oliver

   J King Oliver

19 How old was Armstrong when he went to Chicago?

   Ⓐ 21 or 22

   B 25 or 26

   C 30 or 31

   D 34 or 35

20 Why do people think of Armstrong when they hear the word *jazz*?

   Ⓕ He was a great jazz performer.

   G He did not like jazz music.

   H He was from New Orleans.

   J He had been in trouble as a child.

GO ON

Common Core State Standards

Questions 14, 17, 20: CCSS Informational Text 1. Refer to details and examples in a text when explaining what the text says explicitly and when drawing inferences from the text. **Questions 13, 15–16, 18–19: CCSS Informational Text 7.** Interpret information presented visually, orally, or quantitatively (e.g., in charts, graphs, diagrams, time lines, animations, or interactive elements on Web pages) and explain how the information contributes to an understanding of the text in which it appears.

WRITTEN RESPONSE TO THE SELECTION

> **Look Back and Write** Look back at pages 120–123. Based on what you read, write about what young Jean-François did that enabled him, as an adult, to unlock the key to ancient Egyptian writing. Provide evidence from the selection to support your answer.

The information in the box below will help you remember what you should think about when you write your composition.

REMEMBER—YOU SHOULD

☐ write about what Jean-François did that enabled him to unlock the key to ancient Egyptian writing.

☐ keep your purpose in mind as you write and include only those details that relate directly to your subject.

☐ write a conclusion that lets the reader know you have finished your topic.

☐ try to use correct spelling, capitalization, punctuation, grammar, and sentences.

Common Core State Standards

CCSS Writing 9.b. Apply grade 4 Reading standards to informational texts (e.g., "Explain how an author uses reasons and evidence to support particular points in a text"). (Also **CCSS Informational Text 1.**, **CCSS Writing 2.**, **CCSS Writing 4.**, **CCSS Writing 5.**, **CCSS Writing 9.**, **CCSS Language 1.**, **CCSS Language 2.**)

VOCABULARY

Directions

Find the word or words with the same meaning as the underlined word. Circle the letter next to the answer.

1 We need one more <u>reference</u>.

A method of study

B scientific fact

Ⓒ source of information

D successful business

2 The <u>crime</u> is on tape.

F ballet performance

Ⓖ act of breaking the law

H automobile accident

J party in someone's honor

3 Nina walked past each <u>exhibit</u>.

A carriage

B gallery

Ⓒ display

D open doorway

4 Joseph wrote a report about <u>reptiles</u>.

F animals with hair

G animals with paws

H animals with gills

Ⓙ animals with scales

5 <u>Amphibians</u> are amazing!

Ⓐ animals that live both on land and in water

B animals that eat both meat and plants

C animals that have both beaks and feathers

D animals that hunt during the day and at night

6 I found a <u>salamander</u>.

Ⓕ type of animal

G type of flower

H type of rock

J type of shell

7 Some <u>lizards</u> change colors.

A kinds of birds

B kinds of mammals

C kinds of insects

Ⓓ kinds of reptiles

Common Core State Standards

Questions 1–7: CCSS Language 5.c. Demonstrate understanding of words by relating them to their opposites (antonyms) and to words with similar but not identical meanings (synonyms).

WORD ANALYSIS

Directions
Find the words with the same meaning as the underlined word. Circle the letter next to the answer.

8 The <u>antislavery</u> bill passed in the Senate.

   (F) against slavery

   G for slavery

   H adding more slavery

   J discussing slavery

9 They will perform the play in the <u>amphitheater</u>.

   A very small theater

   B very crowded theater

   (C) theater with seats on all sides of the stage

   D theater that children bring their pets to

10 This <u>antibiotic</u> ointment is very effective.

   F that which has no odor or color

   G that which colors hair

   H that which is sticky or greasy

   (J) that which fights germs

11 I took part in an <u>antiwar</u> protest last week.

   A joining the army

   (B) not wanting war

   C wanting war

   D talking about the military

12 The pet owners marched for <u>anticruelty</u>.

   F related to cruelty

   G in favor of cruelty

   (H) opposed to cruelty

   J not related to cruelty

GO ON

Common Core State Standards

Questions 8–12: Language 4.b. Use common, grade-appropriate Greek and Latin affixes and roots as clues to the meaning of a word (e.g., *telegraph*, *photograph*, *autograph*).

COMPREHENSION

World Travelers

I sat down on my favorite stool at the counter and grinned at Anne Marie. Usually she comes over to chat with me when I come to the diner after school. Today, though, I saw she was too busy to do more than grin back at me. I opened my notebook and began to write. Anne Marie brought me a slice of apple pie, and I absentmindedly ate it as I worked on my story.

"May I sit here?"

I looked up. A stocky, dark-haired boy about my age was smiling at me. "My name's Alejandro," he said. Then I remembered him. He was a Mexican exchange student in my homeroom. Homeroom only met once a week for twenty minutes, so I had seen very little of him.

"My name's Hank," I told him. I shoved my backpack over on the counter to make room for him.

Anne Marie came by with another slice of pie and two big glasses of milk. As Alejandro drank, he looked curiously at my notebook. "What are you writing? Is it homework?"

"I keep a journal," I explained. "I like to write here because there are two new babies at home, and they make a lot of noise! They're cute, but Mom is always wanting me to baby-sit, and I can't do that very well while I'm trying to write. So I come here. What about you? Do you have brothers and sisters back in Mexico?"

"There are no babies, but I have one brother and two sisters," Alejandro answered. "I wanted to come to this country because I am thinking about college. I wanted to see what it was like here and find out about music classes. They aren't so good where I am from, but I think they are very good here."

"Your English is great," I told him. "Much better than my Spanish! I'm going to have to work very hard at learning languages to do what I want to do after I leave school." Alejandro looked interested, so I went on. "I want to be a reporter and travel around the world. My grandmother did that a long time ago. She wrote magazine articles from different countries. She was even on the battlefields during World War II!"

Alejandro grinned. "I would like to meet your grandmother," he said. "I want to be an opera singer. I have wanted to do that ever since I first heard people sing on stage. My mother sings, and she wants me to succeed. So I, too, will travel all over the world!"

GO ON

Directions

Choose the item that best answers each question about the selection you just read. Circle the letter next to the answer.

13 Which sentence accurately compares what Anne Marie and Hank do at the diner?

A Anne Marie is a waitress, and Hank is a waiter.

B Anne Marie does her homework, and Hank writes.

C Anne Marie is a waitress, and Hank is a customer.

D Anne Marie runs the diner, and Hank works there.

14 What does Hank usually do at the diner?

F He hangs out with his friends.

G He writes in his journal.

H He does his homework.

J He interviews people for articles.

15 Alejandro and Hank first met

A in homeroom.

B at the diner.

C at a concert.

D at a soccer game.

16 Both Alejandro and Hank

F are from Mexico.

G like to write.

H are new students at the same school.

J know what they want to do after leaving school.

17 What happens after Hank and Alejandro meet?

A They smile and sit silently together.

B They talk easily together.

C They wait for Anne Marie to join them.

D They get into an argument.

18 What have Hank and Alejandro discovered by the end of the story?

F They don't remember each other from homeroom.

G They are both proficient at foreign languages.

H They have a lot in common.

J They both like Anne Marie.

19 Alejandro and Hank have both come to the diner

A from school.

B from home.

C from soccer practice.

D from choir practice.

20 This story takes place

F in the future.

G two hundred years ago.

H in the present.

J in the far, distant past.

GO ON

Common Core State Standards

Questions 13–20: CCSS Literature 1. Refer to details and examples in a text when explaining what the text says explicitly and when drawing inferences from the text.

WRITTEN RESPONSE TO THE SELECTION

Look Back and Write Look back at pages 151–152. Why does Chief Brown suspect Mrs. King of stealing the salamander? Provide evidence to support your answers.

The information in the box below will help you remember what you should think about when you write your composition.

REMEMBER—YOU SHOULD

☐ explain why Chief Brown suspects Mrs. King of stealing the salamander.

☐ include details that will help the reader understand Chief Brown's thoughts.

☐ reread your response and add or remove words or phrases if something is unclear.

☐ try to use correct spelling, capitalization, punctuation, grammar, and sentences.

GO ON

Common Core State Standards

CCSS Writing 9.a. Apply grade 4 Reading standards to literature (e.g., "Describe in depth a character, setting, or event in a story or drama, drawing on specific details in the text [e.g., a character's thoughts, words, or actions]."). (Also **CCSS Literature 1., CCSS Literature 3., CCSS Writing 4., CCSS Writing 5., CCSS Writing 10., CCSS Language 1., CCSS Language 2.**)

_____

_____

_____

_____

_____

_____

_____

_____

_____

_____

_____

_____

_____

_____

_____

_____

_____

_____

_____

_____

_____

_____

VOCABULARY

Directions

Find the word or words with the same meaning as the underlined word. Circle the letter next to the answer.

1 There is a powerful <u>wind</u> outside.

A rainstorm

B earthquake

Ⓒ air in motion

D smell

2 Are you wearing a <u>parachute</u>?

F wheel used to steer

G military uniform

H large backpack with rockets

Ⓙ cloth canopy used to fall slowly

3 I was <u>concentrating</u> during the class.

Ⓐ paying close attention

B daydreaming

C writing notes

D talking to my friends

4 Fred searched in the <u>underbrush</u>.

F pine forest

G large, sandy desert

H a narrow valley

Ⓙ thick forest shrubs

5 Hard work is <u>essential</u> to good grades.

A optional

Ⓑ necessary

C painful

D hostile

6 Barbara did her job with <u>dedication</u>.

Ⓕ devotion

G good humor

H anger

J carelessness

7 What is the <u>method</u> for completing the project?

A reward

Ⓑ plan

C reason

D equipment

Common Core State Standards

Question 1: CCSS Language 1.g. Correctly use frequently confused words (e.g., *to, too, two; there, their*). **Questions 2–7:**
CCSS Foundational Skills 3.a. Use combined knowledge of all letter-sound correspondences, syllabication patterns, and morphology (e.g., roots and affixes) to read accurately unfamiliar multisyllabic words in context and out of context.

WORD ANALYSIS

Directions

For each sentence, choose the correct meaning of the underlined word. Circle the letter next to the answer.

8 Molly takes <u>ballet</u> lessons.

F type of piano
G type of acting
(H) type of dance
J type of fencing

9 The story was to be <u>continued</u> in next month's issue.

(A) picked up again
B criticized
C dramatized
D begun

10 That alcohol is to be used for <u>medicinal</u> purposes only.

F removing color from hair
G clothes-washing
H furniture refinishing
(J) healing

11 The next scene showed the hero and heroine <u>escaping</u> a river full of deadly crocodiles.

(A) getting away from
B photographing
C fishing in
D going swimming in

12 We stopped at a <u>café</u>.

F grocery store
(G) restaurant
H nightclub
J pizza parlor

COMPREHENSION

The Animal Kingdom

The world is full of many kinds of animals. Some walk on land. Some fly through the air. Some swim in water. The best-known animals are those with backbones. I would like to tell you about the five groups, or classes, of these animals. This chart lists the five classes and their key features.

GO ON

Common Core State Standards

Questions 8–12: CCSS Language 4.a. Use context (e.g., definitions, examples, or restatements in text) as a clue to the meaning of a word or phrase.

122

Weekly Test 21 Unit 5 Week 1

Class	Key Features	Examples
Fish	• Lives in water • Breathes through gills	Trout, sharks
Amphibian	• Has moist, smooth skin • Lives in water and on land	Frogs, salamanders
Reptile	• Has dry, scaly skin • Breathes through lungs	Snakes, turtles
Bird	• Has feathers and wings	Hawks, owls
Mammal	• Has hair or fur • Makes milk to feed young	Elephants, dogs

All fish live in water. They breathe through organs called *gills*. These organs take oxygen from the water. Fish are cold-blooded animals. They cannot control the temperature of their bodies very well. The temperature of their bodies stays about the same as that of the water they live in.

Like fish, amphibians are cold-blooded animals. Most amphibians live the first part of their lives in water, where they breathe through gills. They later move to land and breathe through lungs. But they return to water to lay their eggs.

Like amphibians and fish, reptiles are cold-blooded animals. Many reptiles live in warm places, such as deserts. They rely on the heat of the sun to warm them enough so that they can move about.

Unlike reptiles, amphibians, and fish, birds are warm-blooded. They can control their body temperature, except under extreme conditions. Birds are the only animals with feathers. All birds have wings, and most of them can fly.

Mammals are also warm-blooded creatures. Mammals feed their young with milk made by the mother's body. Humans belong to this class of animals.

Most people like to learn about animals. But we need to do more than just study animals. We need to protect them and the places they live. We're the only animals who can do that.

GO ON

Directions

Choose the item that best answers each question about the selection you just read.
Circle the letter next to the answer.

13 What kind of animal is a frog?

   A reptile

   (B) amphibian

   C fish

   D mammal

14 How do birds differ from all other classes of animals with backbones?

   F They are cold-blooded.

   G They are warm-blooded.

   (H) They have feathers.

   J They produce milk to feed their young.

15 The author's stated purpose in writing this selection is to

   A express personal feelings about animals.

   B persuade readers to adopt pets.

   (C) inform readers about groups of backboned animals.

   D entertain readers with amusing animal stories.

16 Read paragraph 7. What is the author's implied purpose in writing this paragraph?

   F to inform readers about animal protection groups

   (G) to persuade readers to protect animals

   H to entertain readers with unusual facts about animals

   J to express an opinion about people's place in the animal kingdom

17 Which words in paragraph 7 give clues to the author's purpose?

   (A) "We need to protect"

   B "learn about animals"

   C "study animals"

   D "We're the only animals"

18 A key feature of a mammal is that it

   F has large teeth.

   G lives both on land and in water.

   H has scaly skin.

   (J) produces milk to feed its young.

19 In paragraph 3, the author's purpose is to

   (A) explain how amphibians live on land and in water.

   B explain how amphibians are like fish.

   C persuade readers to learn more about fish.

   D persuade readers that amphibians are more interesting than fish.

20 In paragraph 5, the author's purpose is to inform readers about

   F differences between birds and fish.

   G ways in which birds are like all other classes of animals.

   (H) key features of birds.

   J key features of fish, amphibians, reptiles, and birds.

GO ON

Common Core State Standards

Question 13: CCSS Informational Text 7. Interpret information presented visually, orally, or quantitatively (e.g., in charts, graphs, diagrams, time lines, animations, or interactive elements on Web pages) and explain how the information contributes to an understanding of the text in which it appears. **Questions 14, 18: CCSS Informational Text 1.** Refer to details and examples in a text when explaining what the text says explicitly and when drawing inferences from the text. **Questions 15–17, 19–20: CCSS Informational Text 8.** Explain how an author uses reasons and evidence to support particular points in a text.

WRITTEN RESPONSE TO THE SELECTION

Look Back and Write Look back at pages 180–182, the section titled "Extreme Risk." After reading about the life of a smokejumper, do you think the title "Extreme Risk" would have been a better title for the whole article? Why or why not? Provide evidence to support your answer.

The information in the box below will help you remember what you should think about when you write your composition.

REMEMBER—YOU SHOULD

☐ explain whether or not "Extreme Risk" would be a good title for the whole article.

☐ state your opinion at the beginning of your response and restate it at the end.

☐ support your opinion with facts and examples from the article.

☐ try to use correct spelling, capitalization, punctuation, grammar, and sentences.

Common Core State Standards

CCSS Writing 1.a. Introduce a topic or text clearly, state an opinion, and create an organizational structure in which related ideas are grouped to support the writer's purpose. (Also **CCSS Writing 5., CCSS Language 1., CCSS Language 2.**)

VOCABULARY

Directions

Find the word or words with the same meaning as the underlined word. Circle the letter next to the answer.

1 That land has been <u>terraced</u>.

A divided

B reserved

C leveled

D developed

2 The bells made a <u>glorious</u> sound.

F rhythmic

G depressing

H surprising

J magnificent

3 Did you see any <u>ruins</u>?

A jungles

B mountains

C universities

D remains

4 The <u>granite</u> feels cool.

F wood

G rock

H dirt

J water

5 Your <u>curiosity</u> can get you into trouble.

A search for antiques

B desire to know

C need for attention

D lack of knowledge

6 Helena's words came out in a <u>torrent</u>.

F swift flow

G stern manner

H shout

J squeal

7 The foxes hide in the <u>thickets</u>.

A pastures

B caves

C flowers

D shrubs

GO ON

Common Core State Standards

Questions 1–6: CCSS Language 4.b. Use common, grade-appropriate Greek and Latin affixes and roots as clues to the meaning of a word (e.g., *telegraph, photograph, autograph*). **Question 7: CCSS Foundational Skills 3.a.** Use combined knowledge of all letter-sound correspondences, syllabication patterns, and morphology (e.g., roots and affixes) to read accurately unfamiliar multisyllabic words in context and out of context.

Weekly Test 22 Unit 5 Week 2

127

WORD ANALYSIS

Directions
Find the word or words with the same meaning as the underlined word. Circle the letter next to the answer.

8 Dad told us a <u>wondrous</u> bedtime story.

(F) full of wonder

G lacking wonder

H appearing to have wonder

J having a little wonder

9 The new student was <u>teachable</u>.

A not able to be taught

B wanting to be taught

(C) capable of being taught

D not wanting to be taught

10 The plant Jill found was <u>edible</u>.

F only sometimes fit to be eaten

(G) fit to be eaten

H not fit to be eaten

J eaten

11 The jury found the witness <u>believable</u>.

(A) can be believed

B cannot be believed

C partly able to be believed

D hoping to be believed

12 A <u>famous</u> author visited our school.

F having no fame

G looking for fame

H not wanting fame

(J) having much fame

COMPREHENSION

A Noisy Silence

Emma sat down next to Deanna at the cafeteria table. Emma started talking, while Deanna kept on eating her lunch. They had only thirty minutes for lunch and recess. Deanna wanted to get outside quickly to play kickball, but Emma wanted to talk about the new boy in their fourth-grade class. She did not care about playing kickball.

"Collin looks smart, but he never talks," Emma said. "What do you think is wrong with him? He sits with Grant on the bus to school. Grant talks and asks Collin questions sometimes. But Collin never answers."

"He's probably shy because he's new," Deanna answered. "I'd be quiet, too, if I moved to a new school."

GO ON

> **Common Core State Standards**
>
> **Questions 8–12: CCSS Language 4.b.** Use common, grade-appropriate Greek and Latin affixes and roots as clues to the meaning of a word (e.g., *telegraph, photograph, autograph*).

"I wouldn't," said Emma. "I'd want to make friends right away. I'd talk to everybody who was nice to me. Collin doesn't talk to anyone. He doesn't even talk to Ben or Carlos, and they're the friendliest boys in class."

"We should just leave him alone and give him time," said Deanna. "He'll make friends when he's ready."

Deanna finished her lunch and raced outside to play kickball. Emma moved to sit by another girl and slowly ate her sandwich. As she ate and talked, she watched Collin. He was sitting by himself at the end of the line of tables. The other boys had already gone outside for recess.

By the time Emma left the cafeteria, recess was nearly over. Outside, the younger children were using the swings and slides. The older students were on the blacktop, playing kickball and jump rope. A few boys were throwing around a baseball. Collin had followed Emma outside. He walked over to the fence and stood there by himself, leaning against the fence. Emma watched him.

Suddenly, Collin jumped and pointed toward Emma's head. He yelled, "Watch out!"

Emma turned just as a baseball sailed past her face. Grant raced up to her and said, "I'm sorry, Emma. I made a wild throw. It's a good thing you moved, or the ball would have hit your head!"

"It's a good thing Collin warned me," Emma answered. "Those were the first words I've ever heard him say."

"Go easy on Collin," Grant said. "My mom talked to his mom. She found out that Collin stutters. He's afraid to talk. He thinks everyone will make fun of him. We should just give him time."

Just then the bell rang. It was time to go back to class. Emma smiled at Collin and thanked him as they lined up to go back inside. Collin just nodded, but he smiled back.

Emma thought about Collin for the rest of the day. That night she made a decision. She wasn't going to just give Collin time. She was going to do something. She planned to talk to all the kids in their class. She would get them to agree to never make fun of Collin. Then she would talk to Collin. She would tell him that she knew about his problem. She would say it didn't matter, and that she wanted to be his friend. She would tell him that no one would tease him. Emma would NOT just wait. She was going to solve this problem.

GO ON

Directions

Choose the item that best answers each question about the selection you just read. Circle the letter next to the answer.

13 How is Collin different from the other students in the story?

A He isn't as smart.

B He isn't as good at sports.

C He is quieter.

D He is older.

14 How does Grant act toward Collin?

F He shows understanding and patience.

G He makes fun of him.

H He avoids him.

J He encourages Collin to make friends.

15 In what way are Deanna and Grant alike?

A They both love to play kickball.

B They both think Collin needs time.

C They both think Collin is strange.

D They both dislike Emma.

16 What does Emma do after Collin warns her?

F She asks Deanna what is wrong with Collin.

G She asks her teacher what is wrong with Collin.

H She gets hit in the head with a baseball.

J She makes a plan to help Collin.

17 Compared to Deanna, Emma cares less about

A playing kickball at recess.

B helping Collin.

C making good grades.

D making friends.

18 How does Emma differ from Grant in her approach to Collin?

F She is less understanding.

G She wants to take more action.

H She pays less attention to Collin.

J She is less friendly to Collin.

19 In what way are Emma and Collin alike?

A They both dislike kickball.

B They both dislike Grant.

C They both take a lot of time at lunch.

D They both hurry through lunch.

20 Why doesn't Collin talk to his classmates?

F because he is new at school and shy

G because he stutters and fears being teased

H because he doesn't like his classmates

J because he thinks his classmates are mean

GO ON

Common Core State Standards

Questions 13–20: CCSS Informational Text 1. Refer to details and examples in a text when explaining what the text says explicitly and when drawing inferences from the text.

WRITTEN RESPONSE TO THE SELECTION

> **Look Back and Write** Look back at pages 208–209. Why do you think Hiram Bingham considered the old stone wall in Cusco to be such a mystery? Provide evidence to support your answer.

The information in the box below will help you remember what you should think about when you write your composition.

REMEMBER—YOU SHOULD

☐ explain why Hiram Bingham was mystified by the old stone wall in Cusco.

☐ clearly state your answer and support it with facts from the text.

☐ review your answer and think of ways to improve the content and make your writing more interesting.

☐ try to use correct spelling, capitalization, punctuation, grammar, and sentences.

GO ON

Common Core State Standards

CCSS Writing 1. Write opinion pieces on topics or texts, supporting a point of view with reasons and information. (Also **CCSS Informational Text 1., CCSS Language 1. CCSS Language 2.**)

VOCABULARY

Directions

Find the word or words with the same meaning as the underlined word. Circle the letter next to the answer.

1 The hikers <u>trekked</u> across the snow.

(A) traveled slowly

B rappelled

C ran wildly

D slipped

2 The small village lay just beyond the <u>ridge</u>.

(F) narrow chain of hills

G mountain peak

H plateau

J skyscraper

3 Hand me that <u>coil</u> of rope.

A long piece

B very short piece

(C) circular-shaped piece

D lasso

4 Where the old building had been was now a <u>void</u>.

F new structure

G grove of trees

(H) empty space

J large tent

5 Jorge <u>foresaw</u> trouble.

(A) knew beforehand

B started or caused

C avoided

D worried about

6 The mountain climbers were ready for their <u>descent</u>.

F climb up

G picnic

H hike

(J) climb down

7 The <u>shaft</u> led to the roof.

A tall, narrow window

B stairs or a long ladder

(C) long, narrow hole

D door or gate

GO ON

Common Core State Standards

Questions 1–7: CCSS Language 4. Determine or clarify the meaning of unknown and multiple-meaning words and phrases based on *grade 4 reading and content,* choosing flexibly from a range of strategies.

- -

WORD ANALYSIS

Directions

For each sentence, choose the word that is related to the underlined word. Circle the letter next to the answer.

8 The weather <u>forecast</u> is for rain.

- F forty
- (G) foretell
- H forever
- J forget

9 Sam loves his <u>geography</u> class.

- (A) geology
- B germ
- C gemstone
- D gear

10 The house is <u>located</u> beyond those hills.

- F locust
- G locket
- H lockbox
- (J) locality

11 I read the film <u>script</u>.

- A science
- B screen
- (C) description
- D ripped

12 The <u>comedian</u> was very funny.

- F come
- (G) comic
- H company
- J comb

COMPREHENSION

Caught in the Storm

Jeff and Hector were returning home from their hike when they heard a low rumble in the sky. "Sounds like a storm is coming," said Hector as they entered a large field.

"And we still have half a mile to go before we reach your house," said Jeff. "We will get soaked!" But Hector was not as worried about rain as he was about lightning. Just then the sky lit up with a bolt of lightning. It was followed by a loud boom of thunder.

"Yipes!" cried Jeff. "That lightning was pretty close!"

"You're right," replied Hector. "Let's get out of this field. It's dangerous to be in an open

GO ON

Common Core State Standards

Questions 8–12: CCSS Language 4.a. Use context (e.g., definitions, examples, or restatements in text) as a clue to the meaning of a word or phrase.

area when there's a lightning storm." That sounded good to Jeff. They started to run as the first raindrops fell.

"Let's head for those trees over there," said Jeff. "We will be able to stay dry, and we can wait there until it stops raining."

Hector shook his head. "That's not a good idea," he said. "Trees are tall and can attract lightning. We could be struck standing under a tree."

Jeff looked at his friend with surprise. "How do you know so much about lightning?" he asked Hector.

"We learned all about it in science class," said Hector. "The safest place to be in a storm is in a building or a car." Just then another flash of lightning lit up the summer sky. This time the crack of thunder that followed it sounded very close.

Jeff pointed to an old abandoned barn across from the field. "Let's go there," he said. "We will be safe there and dry too."

Hector agreed. The two boys ran into the old barn. They sat down on bales of hay and watched the rain pour down outside. It felt good to be out of the rain. They talked about their hike and waited. Soon the storm passed, and the rain stopped. The sun came out. The boys left the barn and headed for Hector's house.

Hector's mother was very glad to see them come up the walk. "I was worried about you!" she cried. "I was afraid that you would be caught in the storm or maybe even struck by lightning."

Jeff grinned. "No way," he said. "Hector knows all about that. He really pays attention in science class." Then they told her about how they sat out the storm in the barn.

"That was a sensible thing to do," said Hector's mother. "Now you two look as if you could use something to warm you up. How about a cup of hot cocoa?"

Both boys agreed that was a great idea.

Directions

Choose the item that best answers each question about the selection you just read. Circle the letter next to the answer.

13 Where is the story first set?

  A   a forest

  B   a barn

  Ⓒ   a field

  D   Hector's house

14 Why doesn't Hector want to go under the trees?

  Ⓕ   They could be struck by lightning there.

  G   They wouldn't stay dry there.

  H   The trees are too far away.

  J   Hector feels safer in the field.

15 Where do the boys sit out the storm?

  Ⓐ   in an old barn

  B   in an abandoned car

  C   at Hector's house

  D   on a trail

16 From what happens in the story, you can conclude that Hector is

  F   younger than Jeff.

  G   very afraid of lightning.

  H   not very cautious.

  Ⓙ   a good science student.

17 How does Jeff's knowledge of Hector grow by the end of the story?

  Ⓐ   Jeff learns how useful Hector's grasp of science is.

  B   Jeff learns that Hector likes to be the boss.

  C   Jeff learns that Hector's ideas are always better than his own.

  D   Jeff learns that Hector will help him do better in science.

18 What are the boys doing when the storm strikes?

  F   camping

  G   playing tennis

  Ⓗ   hiking

  J   flying kites

19 What is the likeliest reason the author wrote this story?

  A   to persuade and describe

  B   to inform and describe

  Ⓒ   to entertain and inform

  D   to entertain and persuade

20 Which statement best expresses the theme of the story?

  F   It's always good to compromise in order to stay friends.

  Ⓖ   What you learn in school can prove useful in the real world.

  H   You shouldn't believe everything you learn in school.

  J   Parents always worry about their children.

GO ON

Common Core State Standards

Questions 13–18: CCSS Literature 3. Describe in depth a character, setting, or event in a story or drama, drawing on specific details in the text (e.g., a character's thoughts, words, or actions). **Questions 19–20: CCSS Literature 2.** Determine a theme of a story, drama, or poem from details in the text; summarize the text.

WRITTEN RESPONSE TO THE SELECTION

> **Look Back and Write** Look back at pages 238–239. How can you tell that Axel is an experienced mountain climber? Provide evidence to support your answer.

The information in the box below will help you remember what you should think about when you write your composition.

REMEMBER—YOU SHOULD

☐ explain how you know that Axel is an experienced mountain climber.

☐ write one paragraph for each of your main ideas.

☐ choose facts from the text that support each main idea.

☐ try to use correct spelling, capitalization, punctuation, grammar, and sentences.

Common Core State Standards

CCSS Writing 4. Produce clear and coherent writing in which the development and organization are appropriate to task, purpose, and audience. (Also **CCSS Writing 3.d., CCSS Language 1., CCSS Language 2.**)

VOCABULARY

Directions

Find the word or words with the same meaning as the underlined word. Circle the letter next to the answer.

1 We must <u>depart</u> early tomorrow morning.

A complete

B report

C leave

D fiddle

2 They flew from one <u>continent</u> to another.

F landmass

G waterway

H rain forest

J hillside

3 She gave me a <u>forbidding</u> look.

A concerned

B threatening

C puzzled

D doubtful

4 The crane <u>heaves</u> the piano to the second floor.

F hoists

G crushes

H scratches

J buries

5 You could see the <u>anticipation</u> on his face.

A disbelief

B confusion

C determination

D excitement

6 We saw the <u>convergence</u> of the rivers.

F flooding

G widening

H cleaning

J joining

7 <u>Icebergs</u> appear smaller than they really are.

A ice caps that cover the polar regions

B sheets of ice that creep down mountains

C sticks of ice that hang from buildings

D masses of ice that float in the ocean

GO ON

Common Core State Standards

Questions 1–3, 5–7: **CCSS Foundational Skills 3.a.** Use combined knowledge of all letter-sound correspondences, syllabication patterns, and morphology (e.g., roots and affixes) to read accurately unfamiliar multisyllabic words in context and out of context.
Question 4: **CCSS Language 4.** Determine or clarify the meaning of unknown and multiple-meaning words and phrases based on *grade 4 reading and content,* choosing flexibly from a range of strategies.

WORD ANALYSIS

Directions
Find the words with the same meaning as the underlined word. Circle the letter next to the answer.

8 The <u>destruction</u> of the building took several seconds.

   F time of destroying

   (G) act of destroying

   H way of destroying

   J person who destroys

9 Bob was in <u>communication</u> with his brother.

   (A) act of communicating

   B a kind of communicating

   C person who communicates

   D lack of communicating

10 Juan took a class in art <u>appreciation</u>.

   F not appreciating

   G school of appreciating

   (H) act of being appreciated

   J type of appreciating

11 There was an <u>explosion</u> in the mine.

   A time of exploding

   (B) result of exploding

   C thing that is exploding

   D kind of exploding

12 The <u>creation</u> of the painting was a slow process for the artist.

   F absence of creating

   G way of creating

   (H) act of creating

   J dream of creating

COMPREHENSION

Keeping Dying Languages Alive

Did you know that there are about seven thousand languages spoken around the world today? About half of these are spoken by small groups of people. Many of these languages will be gone in the next hundred years as these people die out. Five areas of the world have the largest number of dying languages. They include parts of eastern Russia, northern Australia, and central South America. The two remaining places are in the United States. They are the upper Pacific coast and the Southwest. Nearly all of the languages in these last two places are spoken by groups of Native Americans.

GO ON

| Common Core State Standards |

Questions 8–12: CCSS Language 4.b. Use common, grade-appropriate Greek and Latin affixes and roots as clues to the meaning of a word (e.g., *telegraph, photograph, autograph*).

There are fifty-four Native American languages spoken in the Pacific Northwest, which includes parts of Canada. The most threatened language is Siletz Dee-ni, which is spoken by only one person in the state of Oregon. When that person dies, the language will die also. One group is working to create an online dictionary to preserve this language.

Forty languages are spoken by Native Americans in Texas, Oklahoma, and New Mexico. Only older people speak most of them. Young people learn English in school. Then they enter the world of business where they need to know English. They soon stop speaking their native languages. The Comanche language, for example, is spoken by fewer than nine hundred people. Most of them are old.

Language is more than just words. It tells a lot about a group's values, oral stories, history, and wisdom. Geneva Navarro grew up speaking Comanche to her grandparents and translating English for them. Today, she is sad to see their language dying out. "Our language is our culture," she has said. "It holds our culture together. It tells us who we are and where we came from."

Navarro is helping to keep Comanche alive. She teaches classes in the language to young Native Americans in New Mexico. Other older Comanche people are doing the same. The young people they teach are finding a new pride in their language and their culture. They are protecting their ways in a nation where most people speak English.

The Living Tongues Institute for Endangered Languages is also trying to protect native languages around the world. Institute workers are writing down and recording words in the languages. But it is hard work, and time is running out. The Institute claims that endangered languages are disappearing far more quickly than endangered animals. They say a language disappears about every two weeks!

Directions

Choose the item that best answers each question about the selection you just read. Circle the letter next to the answer.

13 How many of the world's languages are in danger of disappearing?

A a fifth

B a fourth

C three-quarters

D half

14 The main idea in paragraph 4 is that

F language is important to keeping a culture alive.

G Geneva Navarro is sad to see Comanche dying out.

H language involves stories and history.

J grandchildren often translate for their grandparents.

GO ON

Common Core State Standards

Questions 13–14: CCSS Informational Text 2. Determine the main idea of a text and explain how it is supported by key details; summarize the text.

15 From the information in paragraph 2, you can conclude that the language of Siletz Dee-ni

A is making a comeback.

B is still a healthy language.

C is more popular than Comanche.

(D) may soon be forgotten.

16 What can you conclude is the purpose of the Living Tongues Institute?

F to help people learn more languages

G to hasten the end of useless languages

(H) to preserve dying languages

J to keep Native American cultures alive

17 What is the main idea of paragraph 1?

A Many of the world's languages are thriving.

B Languages are dying in central South America.

C There are many Native American languages in the United States.

(D) Many of the world's languages are in trouble.

18 What detail in paragraph 3 supports the idea that languages are disappearing in the Southwest?

F Forty languages are spoken in this region.

(G) Fewer than nine hundred people speak Comanche today.

H Young people learn English as a second language.

J The Southwest includes Texas and New Mexico.

19 Which sentence from the passage states an opinion?

(A) Our language is our culture.

B Five areas of the world have the largest number of dying languages.

C Young people learn English in school.

D Geneva Navarro grew up speaking Comanche to her grandparents.

20 Which statement best expresses the main idea of this selection?

F There are five parts of the world where the most endangered languages are found.

(G) People are trying to save dying languages, but it is a difficult task.

H Language conveys wisdom and values.

J Geneva Navarro is a hero to her people.

GO ON

Common Core State Standards

Questions 15–16, 19: CCSS Informational Text 1. Refer to details and examples in a text when explaining what the text says explicitly and when drawing inferences from the text. **Questions 17–18, 20: CCSS Informational Text 2.** Determine the main idea of a text and explain how it is supported by key details; summarize the text.

WRITTEN RESPONSE TO THE SELECTION

Look Back and Write Look back at page 272. The author and her friends thought they had discovered a new food for humans. What was this food, and why did they think it would be good to eat? What did they think after they tasted it? Provide evidence to support your answer.

The information in the box below will help you remember what you should think about when you write your composition.

REMEMBER—YOU SHOULD

☐ explain what the author believed she and her friends discovered, why they believed it would be good to eat, and their thoughts after tasting it.

☐ make sure to answer all three questions.

☐ paraphrase, or express in your own words, what the author says.

☐ try to use correct spelling, capitalization, punctuation, grammar, and sentences.

GO ON

Common Core State Standards

CCSS Writing 2. Write informative/explanatory texts to examine a topic and convey ideas and information clearly. (Also CCSS Informational Text 3., CCSS Language 1., CCSS Language 2.)

VOCABULARY

Directions

Find the word or words with the same meaning as the underlined word. Circle the letter next to the answer.

1 The astronauts came upon a <u>rille</u> they could not pass.

 A forked path in a forest

 B rocky ledge on a cliff

 Ⓒ long narrow crack in the ground

 D high dunes in a desert

2 Her puppy was the <u>runt</u> of the litter.

 F smartest

 Ⓖ smallest

 H strongest

 J sweetest

3 The cat <u>taunted</u> the dog.

 Ⓐ teased

 B scratched

 C chased

 D ignored

4 The team <u>trudged</u> across the field.

 F jogged quickly

 G scattered excitedly

 Ⓗ walked slowly

 J shuffled loudly

5 Look for the <u>trench</u> in the pasture.

 A boulder

 Ⓑ ditch

 C creek

 D crater

6 Laura is <u>summoning</u> the others.

 F taking care of

 G looming over

 H giving praise to

 Ⓙ calling upon

7 The injured man <u>staggered</u> away.

 A crept

 Ⓑ stumbled

 C jerked

 D slithered

GO ON

Common Core State Standards

Questions 1–7: CCSS Language 5.c. Demonstrate understanding of words by relating them to their opposites (antonyms) and to words with similar but not identical meanings (synonyms).

WORD ANALYSIS

Directions

For each sentence, choose the correct meaning of the word that is underlined. Circle the letter next to the answer.

8 Polly's sister is in <u>kindergarten</u>.

    F high school

    G college

    H summer camp

    J school for young children

9 Would you like some <u>sauerkraut</u>?

    A cooked cabbage

    B pickles

    C hot dogs

    D beet soup

10 The Johnsons live in the <u>hinterlands</u>.

    F city

    G neighborhood

    H north country

    J remote area

11 We have a <u>dachshund</u> for a pet.

    A long-haired cat

    B colorful bird

    C long, short dog

    D big rabbit

12 Jake stopped at the <u>delicatessen</u>.

    F sporting goods store

    G department store

    H store selling meat and cheese

    J ice cream shop

COMPREHENSION

Leaving Earth

Melinda and her parents stood in the long line of people waiting to board the rocket ship. They had been waiting for more than an hour. Slowly they moved forward, closer and closer to the front of the line. Melinda thought of all she would be leaving behind on Earth: her neighborhood, her house, and her friends. Many of them were leaving Earth too, but they would be going to different parts of the new planet. She might never see them again there.

GO ON

Common Core State Standards

Questions 8–12: CCSS Language 4.a. Use context (e.g., definitions, examples, or restatements in text) as a clue to the meaning of a word or phrase.

For hundreds of years the people of Earth knew their planet was dying. They had failed to take care of it. They had polluted its air and water. They had stripped the land and left their trash everywhere. Now it was too late to save the Earth. The only way for people to survive was to move to another planet. There they would have to start over. They would build homes and towns and make roads. Melinda's parents saw it as a challenge. Melinda didn't know if she wanted to be a settler in a new world.

"It looks as if the rocket ship will be full of people before we get to the front of the line," said Melinda's mother.

"Don't worry," said Melinda's father. "It's a big rocket. There is still plenty of room." But as they drew closer and closer to the front of the line, even her father looked worried. Maybe it would be full before they got on board. If so, they would have to wait for weeks for the next rocket to leave Earth. Melinda held her father's hand tightly as they waited.

"How many in your party?" said a guard when they finally reached the front of the line.

"Just the three of us," said Melinda's father.

The guard grinned. "This is your lucky day," he said. "There are just three seats left on the ship. Come aboard."

Melinda's father smiled at her mother and Melinda. They followed the guard up the ramp to the entrance of the ship. Melinda could hear the cries of disappointment from the people in line behind them. Those people would not be leaving Earth today.

Melinda and her parents took their seats and put on their seatbelts. Soon the pilot announced the takeoff. They gripped the armrests as the rocket ship zoomed upward into space. "Here we go," said Melinda's father. "Off to a new planet and a wonderful new life."

"It's exciting, isn't it?" said her mother.

Melinda nodded, but she didn't feel very excited. She felt sad. She couldn't forget all that she was leaving behind on Earth. She stared out the window of the ship at the Earth below. "If we'd only taken better care of you," she said quietly to the Earth. She watched it grow smaller and smaller until it was only a tiny dot in the vastness of space.

Directions

Choose the item that best answers each question about the selection you just read. Circle the letter next to the answer.

13 What are Melinda and her parents doing at the beginning of the story?

A landing on another planet in a rocket ship

(B) waiting in line to board a rocket ship

C packing their bags for a long trip overseas

D boarding a boat to leave the country

14 Where is the family headed at the end of the story?

F to a new city

G to a new country

H to a new continent

(J) to a new planet

15 How does Melinda show that she depends on her father?

(A) She holds his hand tightly as they wait in line.

B She shares his excitement about their new life.

C She asks him to stay behind with her.

D She changes her feelings and agrees with him.

16 How does Melinda respond when her parents express their excitement?

F She cries and says she doesn't want to leave.

G She smiles and says she's excited too.

(H) She nods and keeps her sad feelings to herself.

J She gets mad and says they ruined Earth.

17 Which word best describes Melinda's character in the story?

(A) uncertain

B angry

C thoughtful

D happy

18 Why is the family leaving Earth?

F It is too crowded.

(G) It is a dying planet.

H Melinda's parents dislike their neighbors.

J Melinda's father has a new job on another planet.

19 Which character expresses the most hope about the future?

A Melinda

B Melinda's mother

(C) Melinda's father

D the pilot of the rocket ship

20 Which sentence best expresses the theme of this story?

F Space travel can be exciting.

(G) People should take better care of the Earth.

H It is hard to start over in a new place.

J Some people are luckier than others.

GO ON

Common Core State Standards

Questions 13–19: CCSS Literature 3. Describe in depth a character, setting, or event in a story or drama, drawing on specific details in the text (e.g., a character's thoughts, words, or actions). **Question 20: CCSS Literature 2.** Determine a theme of a story, drama, or poem from details in the text; summarize the text.

WRITTEN RESPONSE TO THE SELECTION

> **Look Back and Write** Look back at pages 303–304. How do Gerry's actions and thoughts show he is both brave and smart? Provide evidence to support your answer.

The information in the box below will help you remember what you should think about when you write your composition.

REMEMBER—YOU SHOULD

☐ explain why Gerry's actions and thoughts show him to be brave and smart.

☐ include your opinions as well as facts from the story.

☐ vary your sentences by beginning some with phrases, or groups of words, that tell *when* or *where*.

☐ try to use correct spelling, capitalization, punctuation, grammar, and sentences.

Common Core State Standards

CCSS Literature 3. Describe in depth a character, setting, or event in a story or drama, drawing on specific details in the text (e.g., a character's thoughts, words, or actions). (Also **CCSS Writing 2.**, **CCSS Language 1.**, **CCSS Language 2.**)

VOCABULARY

Directions Find the word or words with the same meaning as the underlined word. Circle the letter next to the answer.

1 We met the <u>minister</u> this morning.
- (A) church leader
- B traveling musician
- C sports coach
- D speech writer

2 Ophelia is researching her <u>ancestors</u>.
- F future business goals
- G favorite activities
- H summer vacation
- (J) past family members

3 They have been in business for <u>generations</u>.
- (A) about 30-year periods
- B about 100-year periods
- C about 2-year periods
- D about 5-year periods

4 The hen is <u>shielding</u> her chicks.
- F admiring
- (G) protecting
- H parading
- J grooming

5 I <u>avoided</u> that cliff.
- A drew pictures of
- B paid attention to
- (C) stayed away from
- D climbed down from

6 Please put the table by the <u>pulpit</u>.
- F entrance
- (G) platform
- H bookcase
- J microphone

7 John gave us <u>numerous</u> excuses.
- (A) many
- B excellent
- C ridiculous
- D annoying

/ **Common Core State Standards** \

Questions 1–3, 6–7: CCSS Language 4.b. Use common, grade-appropriate Greek and Latin affixes and roots as clues to the meaning of a word (e.g., *telegraph, photograph, autograph*). **Questions 4–5: CCSS Foundational Skills 3.a.** Use combined knowledge of all letter-sound correspondences, syllabication patterns, and morphology (e.g., roots and affixes) to read accurately unfamiliar multisyllabic words in context and out of context.

WORD ANALYSIS

Directions

For each sentence, choose the correct meaning of the word that is underlined. Circle the letter next to the answer.

8 The <u>generator</u> started to hum and whirl.

   F machine that keeps things cold

   G machine that computes figures

   (H) machine that produces energy

   J machine that carries goods

9 Sam bought a <u>portable</u> television.

   A large screen

   B capable of running on electricity

   (C) capable of being carried

   D color

10 The human body has <u>generative</u> abilities.

   F failing

   (G) reproductive

   H hidden

   J misleading

11 The <u>porter</u> met us at the hotel door.

   (A) baggage carrier

   B manager

   C chef

   D owner

12 The <u>portage</u> was between two rivers.

   F vast forest

   G boat trip

   H parade of people on floats

   (J) carrying of goods overland

GO ON

Common Core State Standards

Questions 8–12: CCSS Language 4.b. Use common, grade-appropriate Greek and Latin affixes and roots as clues to the meaning of a word (e.g., *telegraph, photograph, autograph*).

COMPREHENSION
Rita Moreno: A Show Business Success

Only one actress has won the four biggest awards in show business. Rita Moreno earned the Oscar, the Tony, the Emmy, and the Grammy. She had to work hard for these awards and to reach the top of the entertainment world.

Moreno was born Rosa Alverio in 1931 in Puerto Rico. She came to New York City to live with her mother when she was five years old. The family was poor. Rosa earned money for them by dancing and singing in a department store. She went to Hollywood as a teenager. There she worked dubbing voices in American films for Spanish-speaking viewers. She really wanted to be a movie actress. Finally she made her first film in 1950. Because she was from Puerto Rico, Moreno was given exotic parts. She played Native Americans, Mexicans, and even Asians. Most of these parts were silly and not real. They were stereotypes of these peoples. Moreno didn't like playing such parts, but few other roles were open to her.

Her big break came in the movie *West Side Story*. It was about gangs of young whites and Puerto Ricans. The people in the movie were real. Moreno played the girlfriend of the Puerto Rican gang leader. She acted and also got to sing and dance. She won an Oscar for her part. She was only the second Puerto Rican to win for acting.

Moreno thought she would now get better parts in movies. But she did not. She was still offered exotic parts. She refused to take them and moved back to New York City. There she appeared in plays. Then she met a doctor, Leonard Gordon. They fell in love and were married. They are still married today and have a daughter.

In 1975 Moreno was offered the part of a funny Latin singer in a new play called *The Ritz*. She enjoyed having fun with the kind of parts she was once restricted to. She won a Tony Award for her performance. Moreno has played many roles on television. In 1977 she was a guest on *The Muppet Show* and won an Emmy for her appearance.

Rita Moreno had one more honor to win. In 1995 she received a star on the Hollywood Walk of Fame. After the ceremony Moreno said, "I have been dreaming of this since I was six!" Through hard work and determination, Rita Moreno made her dreams come true. Today she is a role model for young Latino actors and actresses.

GO ON

Directions

Choose the item that best answers each question about the selection you just read. Circle the letter next to the answer.

13 Why did young Rosa dance and sing in a department store?

A for the fun of it

B to be seen and get hired for the movies

C to get free clothes

(D) to earn money for her family

14 Moreno got her big break appearing in

F *The Ritz.*

(G) *West Side Story.*

H *The Muppet Show.*

J a department store.

15 Why was Moreno given silly exotic parts?

A because she was a bad actress

(B) because she was from Puerto Rico

C because she asked for them

D because she was beautiful

16 Which of the following details does not support the main idea that Rita Moreno has had to work hard to achieve success in her career?

F She refused to continue to play exotic roles and went to New York to appear in plays.

G She worked a great deal on television, in addition to appearing in plays.

(H) *West Side Story* is about gangs of young whites and Puerto Ricans.

J She worked at a young age to earn money to help her family.

17 Moreno was unable to get better parts after winning an Oscar. What effect did this have on her?

(A) She moved back to New York to act in plays.

B She quit show business.

C She married a doctor.

D She only did television after that.

18 For her role in *The Ritz,* Moreno won

F an Oscar.

G an Emmy.

(H) a Tony.

J a Grammy.

19 Why did Moreno dub voices for movies?

A so English audiences could understand the words

(B) so Spanish viewers could understand them

C so she could pay for a trip to Puerto Rico

D so she didn't have to work as an actress

20 What caused Moreno to say, "I have been dreaming of this since I was six"?

(F) receiving a star on the Hollywood Walk of Fame

G winning a Grammy

H winning an Oscar for the movie *West Side Story*

J having a daughter

GO ON

Common Core State Standards

Questions 13–20: CCSS Informational Text 3. Explain events, procedures, ideas, or concepts in a historical, scientific, or technical text, including what happened and why, based on specific information in the text.

WRITTEN RESPONSE TO THE SELECTION

> **Look Back and Write** Look back at pages 338 and 339. Find an example of how Martin's father "practiced what he preached." Then write what that example meant to the King family. Provide evidence to support your answer.

The information in the box below will help you remember what you should think about when you write your composition.

REMEMBER—YOU SHOULD

- ☐ explain how Martin's father "practiced what he preached."

- ☐ use both facts and opinions to support your answer.

- ☐ end with a statement that points out the importance of Martin's father's actions.

- ☐ try to use correct spelling, capitalization, punctuation, grammar, and sentences.

GO ON

Common Core State Standards

CCSS Writing 2.b. Develop the topic with facts, definitions, concrete details, quotations, or other information and examples related to the topic. (Also **CCSS Informational Text 1., CCSS Writing 2., CCSS Writing 4., CCSS Writing 5., CCSS Language 1., CCSS Language 2.**)

_____
_____
_____
_____
_____
_____
_____
_____
_____
_____
_____
_____
_____
_____
_____
_____
_____
_____
_____
_____
_____
_____
_____

VOCABULARY

*D*irections

Find the word or words with the same meaning as the underlined word. Circle the letter next to the answer.

1 Daniel has more <u>endurance</u> than anyone I know.

  Ⓐ strength to continue

  B natural talent

  C determination to win

  D muscle control

2 This highway leads to the <u>reservation</u>.

  F lake that has been created by a dam

  G private property that has been sold

  Ⓗ public land that has been set aside

  J valley that has been made by a glacier

3 Thomas went to <u>boarding school</u> last year.

  A a school where groups of students work as teams

  B a school where students learn from carpenters

  C a school where all the students are in one classroom

  Ⓓ a school where students live away from home

4 Beth stayed in a <u>dormitory</u>.

  F farmhouse

  Ⓖ student house

  H guest house

  J clubhouse

5 Prisoners are sometimes forced to do <u>manual labor</u>.

  A done by a student

  B done by machine

  C done by a group

  Ⓓ done by hand

6 <u>Society</u> demands that we follow certain rules.

  F all soldiers

  Ⓖ all people

  H all teachers

  J all coaches

GO ON

Common Core State Standards

Questions 1–6: CCSS Language 4. Determine or clarify the meaning of unknown and multiple-meaning words and phrases based on *grade 4 reading and content,* choosing flexibly from a range of strategies.

WORD ANALYSIS

Directions

For each sentence, choose the correct meaning of the word that is underlined. Circle the letter next to the answer.

7 The coat is made of <u>durable</u> cloth.

  A fancy

  B colorful

  C inexpensive

  (**D**) long-lasting

8 Maria tried to <u>inject</u> a comment into the conversation.

  F disapprove of

  G ignore

  (**H**) throw in

  J take back

9 The man was <u>ejected</u> from the room.

  (**A**) thrown out

  B called

  C absent

  D followed

10 The athlete <u>endured</u> the competition.

  F failed repeatedly

  (**G**) lasted through

  C worried about

  J finished quickly

11 We stayed for the <u>duration</u> of the movie.

  A beginning

  B ending

  (**C**) entire length

  D intermission

12 Todd was <u>rejected</u> by the army.

  F accepted

  G honored

  H ordered

  (**J**) refused

COMPREHENSION

Golf and Tennis

Golf and tennis are very popular sports in the United States. Both sports are usually played by single players. They are not usually team sports, although there are doubles matches in tennis.

Tennis is played on a court where the players face each other across a net. The surface of the court can be grass, clay, or asphalt. An asphalt court is often called a hard court. Golf is played on a large grassy field, called a course, that can be full of obstacles that the players must avoid.

GO ON

Common Core State Standards

Questions 7–12: CCSS Language 4.b. Use common, grade-appropriate Greek and Latin affixes and roots as clues to the meaning of a word (e.g., *telegraph*, *photograph*, *autograph*).

Playing both tennis and golf involves hitting a ball. A golfer hits a golf ball along the ground with a club. The player who gets his ball into eighteen holes over the golf course with the lowest number of club swings is the winner. A tennis player hits a tennis ball over a net with a racket, while the other player hits it back. The winner in a tennis game scores the most points by hitting the ball over the net and within the lines on the court that the other player misses.

While both of these sports are very popular in the United States, they were first played in Europe. Most historians believe the modern version of golf originated in Scotland around the twelfth century. It is believed that the version of tennis played today was invented by an Englishman during the 1870s. He based it on a much older game that was played in Europe, especially France.

Both sports take great skill to play well. Professional golf and tennis are played in big tournaments. In a tennis tournament, the players who lose drop out, and those who win go on to play more games. In the end there are only two finalists left. They play for the championship. In a golf tournament, players usually play on the same course over several days. The golfer who reaches the final hole with the fewest strokes is the champion.

Tennis and golf are popular all over the world. Few other sports are as international as they are. The four major tennis tournaments each year are known as the *Grand Slam*. They are played in the United States, England, France, and Australia. Golf tournaments are also played all over the world, but most of the biggest ones are played in the United States.

Which sport would you rather play—tennis or golf? Maybe you'd like to try both! Golf is much easier to learn than tennis is. However, tennis is more fun than golf. Tennis also is more strenuous, which means it takes more energy to play. Anyone who wants to stay fit should play tennis rather than golf. If you want to relax, however, golf is probably the sport for you.

GO ON

Directions

Choose the item that best answers each question about the selection you just read. Circle the letter next to the answer.

13 Golf and tennis are similar because they

   A are played on a court.

   B involve strenuous exercise.

   C are played with rackets.

   (D) are played by hitting a ball.

14 Which sentence is a statement of fact?

   F Which sport would you rather play—tennis or golf?

   (G) A golfer hits a golf ball along the ground with a club.

   H Golf is much easier to learn than tennis is.

   J If you want to relax, golf is probably the sport for you.

15 Which sentence is a statement of opinion?

   A The golfer who reaches the final hole with the fewest strokes is the champion.

   B The four major tennis tournaments each year are known as the *Grand Slam*.

   (C) Anyone who wants to stay fit should play tennis rather than golf.

   D Most historians believe the modern version of golf originated in Scotland around the twelfth century.

16 How could you verify that sentence 1 in paragraph 6 is a statement of fact?

   F travel around the world

   (G) look up *tennis* and *golf* in an encyclopedia

   H ask a tennis player and a golfer

   J read a story about a tennis player

17 Read paragraph 6. You can conclude that professional golf is most popular in

   A France.

   B England.

   (C) the United States.

   D Scotland.

18 What opinion about golf does the author express?

   F Few young people play golf.

   G Golf is tiring to play.

   C Golf is for professionals only.

   (J) Golf is an easy, relaxing sport.

19 "While both of these sports are very popular in the United States, they were first played in Europe" is

   (A) a statement of fact.

   B a statement of opinion.

   C neither a fact nor an opinion.

   D a statement that contains both fact and opinion.

20 Unlike tennis, the winner in golf must achieve

   F the highest score.

   G the longest shot.

   (H) the lowest score.

   J the perfect game.

GO ON

Common Core State Standards

Questions 13, 17, 20: CCSS Informational Text 2. Determine the theme of a story, drama, or poem from details in the text; summarize the text. **Questions 14–16, 18–19: CCSS Informational Text 1.** Refer to details and examples in a text when explaining what the text says explicitly and when drawing inferences from the text.

WRITTEN RESPONSE TO THE SELECTION

> **Look Back and Write** Reread pages 370 and 371. During his life, many people believed that Jim Thorpe was the greatest athlete in the world. Provide evidence from the time line on these pages to find examples of Jim Thorpe's greatness.

The information in the box below will help you remember what you should think about when you write your composition.

REMEMBER—YOU SHOULD

☐   provide evidence from the time line to find examples of Jim Thorpe's athletic greatness.

☐   tell events in the order in which they occurred.

☐   write persuasively to convince your reader of your position.

☐   try to use correct spelling, capitalization, punctuation, grammar, and sentences.

Common Core State Standards

CCSS Informational Text 7. Interpret information presented visually, orally, or quantitatively (e.g., charts, graphs, diagrams, time lines, animations, or interactive elements on Web pages) and explain how the information contributes to an understanding of the text in which it appears. (Also **CCSS Writing 2.**, **CCSS Writing 2.b.**, **CCSS Writing 4.**, **CCSS Writing 5.**, **CCSS Language 1.**, **CCSS Language 2.**)

VOCABULARY

Directions

Find the word or words with the same meaning as the underlined word. Circle the letter next to the answer.

1 There is a <u>resemblance</u> between the siblings.

   A medical emergency

   B similar appearance

   C remarkable strength

   D musical performance

2 The <u>colonel</u> is waiting.

   F military officer

   G football coach

   H office manager

   J news reporter

3 This river <u>affords</u> water for several communities.

   A splashes

   B drains

   C pollutes

   D provides

4 Let's stay in this <u>quaint</u> hotel.

   F well-known

   G amusingly odd

   H nice-looking

   J covered with paint

5 I saw a <u>glint</u> in his eye.

   A contact lens

   B gray lint

   C brightness

   D speck of dirt

6 My cat was <u>lurking</u> behind the chair.

   F relaxing

   G strutting

   H prancing

   J prowling

7 These <u>palettes</u> need to be cleaned.

   A stirring wands for paints

   B large tubes for paints

   C mixing boards for paints

   D soft brushes for paints

GO ON

Common Core State Standards

Questions 1–7: **CCSS Foundational Skills 4.c** Use context to confirm or self-correct word recognition and understanding, rereading as necessary.

WORD ANALYSIS

*D*irections

For each sentence, choose the correct meaning of the word that is underlined. Circle the letter next to the answer.

8 Carrie is a <u>blonde</u>.

(F) fair-haired woman

G dark-haired woman

H slim woman

J young woman

9 The bride smiled as she tossed her <u>bouquet</u> to the guests that had assembled.

(A) arrangement of flowers

B piece of cake

C lace worn on the head

D doll dressed in white

10 Barry was so proud of his <u>collage</u> that he put it up in his room.

F certificate of achievement

G collectible action figure

(H) picture made by assembling things

J award for writing

11 We waited for Roger at the <u>depot</u>.

A town hall

(B) train station

C crossroads

D market

12 The artist never cleaned his <u>palette</u>.

F studio

G wall for displaying art

H small kitchen area

(J) board for mixing paints

COMPREHENSION

Last Inning

It was the last inning of the big baseball game. The Tigers were winning over the Giants 2–1. The Giants were up at bat with two outs. Jim was on second base. He had hit a double. Then the next batter struck out. Now it was up to Jerry Smith to get a hit. If he didn't, the game would be over, and the Giants would lose.

Jerry was the smallest member of his team. He stepped up to home plate and swung his bat. The pitcher, Tommy Riley, smiled. He knew that Jerry wasn't a good hitter. Most times

GO ON

Common Core State Standards

Questions 8–12: CCSS Language 4. Determine or clarify the meaning of unknown words and phrases based on *grade 4 reading and content,* choosing flexibly from a range of strategies.

at bat, he struck out. Tommy wound up for the pitch. It was a fastball. Jerry swung wildly at the ball. "Strike one!" cried the umpire from behind the plate.

The other Giants shook their heads. They wished that anyone but Jerry were at bat right now. Jerry tried to stay calm. *I'll hit it this time,* he thought to himself.

Tommy's smile looked mean now. Jerry felt that Tommy was making fun of him. He tried to stay focused. The pitch came. The ball went wide, but Jerry swung anyway and missed it. "Strike two!" cried the umpire.

The smile on Tommy Riley's face was huge. He looked around at the other Tigers and shook his head. They knew the game was about to end. They would be the winners. Jerry's teammates looked sad and beaten. They did not think Jerry would hit the ball either. But Jerry didn't give up. He was going to show them all. He calmed himself again as the pitcher got ready. He tried to relax his body. He took a couple of deep breaths. Then he leaned over the plate with his bat held high above his shoulder.

Tommy threw the ball. It zipped straight over the plate. Jerry waited and swung. He smacked the ball hard. It sailed into the air. Tommy looked up in surprise as he watched it go over his head. Jim started running for third base. Jerry was so surprised that he didn't even move! Then he heard his teammates yelling for him to run.

He started for first base. By the time he got there, Jim was coming into home plate. The outfielder was running for the ball. With his teammates cheering him, Jerry kept running. He reached second base. And then he rounded third base. The outfielder threw the ball to Tommy, but not in time. Jerry came tearing across home plate. His teammates were cheering wildly. They had won the game!

The other Giants gathered around Jerry. Mr. Lopez, their coach, pushed his way through the crowd. He gave Jerry a big hug. "Great work, Jerry!" he cried. "You did it, and I didn't think you could."

It was Jerry's turn to smile. "I guess I was the only one who knew I could," he said.

GO ON

Directions

Choose the item that best answers each question about the selection you just read. Circle the letter next to the answer.

13 What happens in the last inning when the Giants are at bat with two outs and a runner on second base?

(A) Jerry Smith comes up to bat.

B Tommy Riley enters the game to pitch.

C Jim hits a double.

D The next batter strikes out.

14 Which event happens first?

F Jerry hits a home run.

G Coach Lopez hugs Jerry.

(H) Jerry swings at two pitches and misses.

J Jerry smacks the ball hard.

15 How is Jerry different from his teammates?

A He is a much better hitter than any of them.

B He is afraid of the pitcher, and they are not.

C He wants to win the game, and they do not.

(D) He believes he can hit the ball, and they do not.

16 The best word to describe Tommy Riley is

F funny.

G desperate.

(H) overconfident.

J angry.

17 Jerry surprises everyone when he hits a

A single.

B double.

C triple.

(D) home run.

18 What does Jerry do just before he gets the third pitch?

(F) He relaxes and takes some deep breaths.

G He looks at his mother in the stands.

H He starts for first base.

J He looks at his coach for a sign.

19 What does Jerry do just after he hits the ball?

A He races around the bases.

B He tells his coach he knew he could do it.

(C) He stands still in surprise.

D He hugs his coach and teammates.

20 Which event happens last?

F Jerry tears across home plate.

(G) Jerry smiles and says he knew he could do it.

H The other Giants crowd around Jerry.

J Coach Lopez gives Jerry a big hug.

GO ON

Common Core State Standards

Questions 13–20: CCSS Literature 1. Refer to details and examples in a text when explaining what the text says explicitly and when drawing inferences from the text.

WRITTEN RESPONSE TO THE SELECTION

Look Back and Write Look back at page 390. Miguel finds something that helps him learn about Colonel Charlebois's past. Write about what Miguel finds out and why it is important to understanding the Colonel's change of heart at the end of the story. How do you think the Colonel and Miguel's family will get along in the future?

The information in the box below will help you remember what you should think about when you write your composition.

REMEMBER—YOU SHOULD

☐ explain what Miguel finds out about the Colonel and why it is important to understanding the Colonel's change of heart.

☐ be sure to answer the question, predicting what the relationship between the Colonel and Miguel's family will be in the future.

☐ introduce your idea in the first paragraph, include facts and examples to support your idea in the second paragraph, and offer your opinion in the third paragraph.

☐ try to use correct spelling, capitalization, punctuation, grammar, and sentences.

GO ON

Common Core State Standards

CCSS Literature 3. Describe in depth a character, setting, or event in a story or drama, drawing on specific details in the text (e.g., a character's thoughts, words, or actions). (Also **CCSS Literature 1., CCSS Writing 2., CCSS Writing 4., CCSS Writing 5., CCSS Language 1., CCSS Language 3.**)

VOCABULARY

Directions

Find the word or words with the same meaning as the underlined word. Circle the letter next to the answer.

1 The **backdrop** showed a sunlit mountain valley.

  A   props on the floor of a stage

  (B) painted cloth at the back of a stage

  C   sign at the front of a theater

  D   poster advertising a play

2 The sheep **graze** in a different pasture each day.

  F   drink water

  G   find grain

  (H) eat grass

  J   take naps

3 The accident left Liza in state of **shock**.

  (A) feeling disturbed

  B   great excitement

  C   feeling tired

  D   feeling hungry

4 The minister put on the **ceremonial** robe.

  F   used for educational purposes

  (G) used for religious or special occasions

  H   used for scientific purposes

  J   used for physical labor

5 All the crops died because of the **drought**.

  A   long rainy period

  B   period of heavy snow

  C   sudden hail

  (D) long period without rain

6 An **abundance** of food was spread across the tables.

  F   very small amount

  G   expensive type

  (H) very large amount

  J   unusual kind

GO ON

Common Core State Standards

Questions 1–6: CCSS Language 4. Determine of clarify the meaning of unknown words and phrases based on *grade 4 reading and content,* choosing flexibly from a range of strategies.

WORD ANALYSIS

Directions

For each sentence, choose the correct word that is related to the underlined word. Circle the letter next to the answer.

7 The spring gushed forth with great <u>abundance.</u>

A density

B undoing

(C) abundantly

D boundaries

8 The <u>pianist</u> played with the orchestra.

(F) piano

G patio

H pickle

J annual

9 Shelly is never <u>resistant</u> to try new things.

A restorative

(B) resistance

C standard

D anthology

10 Hank's father will <u>serve</u> the food.

F secret

(G) servant

H veer

J seek

11 How can you be <u>irreverent</u> about such an important subject?

(A) reverence

B irregular

C revealing

D verify

12 I read the new <u>publication.</u>

F pudding

G blimp

H vacation

(J) publisher

COMPREHENSION

Too Much Television

Lamar thought his family watched too much television. He thought it was a big problem.

"We could do other things if we watched TV less," Lamar said to his sister. "I could read more books. You could play the piano. Mom would have more time for gardening. Dad could get back to lifting weights. We could play cards and other games together. We'd be more active if we weren't always watching TV."

GO ON

Common Core State Standards

Questions 7–12: CCSS Language 4. Determine of clarify the meaning of unknown words and phrases based on *grade 4 reading and content,* choosing flexibly from a range of strategies.

Weekly Test 29 Unit 6 Week 4

"You're right," said Brandi. "Let's keep track of how much TV we watch in a week. We can show it to Mom and Dad. Then we can make some changes."

Lamar and Brandi kept a record for one week. They wrote down how many hours each family member watched television. They made this chart.

Hours Spent Watching TV in a Week

	Lamar	Brandi	Mom	Dad
Monday	2	3	2	3
Tuesday	3	3	1	0
Wednesday	2	2	1	2
Thursday	2	2	2	3
Friday	2	3	2	2
Saturday	4	4	3	5
Sunday	4	5	5	5
Total	19	22	16	20

Lamar and Brandi were shocked when they added up everyone's hours for the week. They showed the chart to their parents. It shocked their parents too.

"I spent almost a full day's time watching TV," said their father. "I would never have believed it. I could do a lot in 20 hours each week."

"Brandi and I have a plan," said Lamar. "What if we all watch one less hour of TV each day during the week? We can each do something else we like. Then on the weekend, we can take two hours each day. We can do something together on Saturday and Sunday. We could play basketball or go fishing."

"That sounds like a great plan, Lamar. I'm proud of you and Brandi for thinking of it," said their mother. "You saw a problem, and you took action. You did something that your Dad and I should have done."

Lamar's plan worked even better than he thought it would. After a month, everyone in the family was spending only about one hour a day watching TV. They had broken their TV habit! They enjoyed all the activities they were doing, alone and together. They didn't even miss TV.

GO ON

Directions

Choose the item that best answers each question about the selection you just read. Circle the letter next to the answer.

13 Who watches TV the most?

(A) Brandi

B Lamar

C Mom

D Dad

14 Who watches TV the least?

F Brandi

G Lamar

(H) Mom

J Dad

15 When do all the family members watch the most TV?

A Monday

B Wednesday

C Friday

(D) Weekend

16 What happens after Lamar and Brandi show their parents the chart?

(F) The family agrees to a plan to watch TV less.

G The family spends more hours watching TV.

H Lamar talks to Brandi about a problem.

J Brandi records the hours that she watches TV.

17 Which word best describes how Lamar and Brandi act?

A sneaky

(B) responsible

C kind

D lazy

18 Which word best describes how Lamar's parents act?

F angry

G sad

(H) supportive

J disappointed

19 Lamar thinks that TV-watching

(A) makes his family less active.

B causes family arguments.

C is educational.

D is the best way to spend free time.

20 How does the family's life change?

F They spend most of their time away from home.

G They are often bored because they aren't watching TV.

(H) They spend more time in activities and less time watching TV.

J The children get higher grades, and the parents get new jobs.

GO ON

Common Core State Standards

Questions 13–20: CCSS Literature 1. Refer to details and examples in a text when explaining what the text says explicitly and when drawing inferences from the text.

WRITTEN RESPONSE TO THE SELECTION

Look Back and Write Look back at pages 422–423. The structure of a play is very different from that of a story. What things does an author include in a play that would not be in a story? Provide evidence to support your answer.

The information in the box below will help you remember what you should think about when you write your composition.

REMEMBER—YOU SHOULD

☐ identify things an author includes in a play that he or she would not include in a story.

☐ use specific details in your answer, explaining how each of the features helps the reader better understand a play.

☐ compare and contrast what you already know about stories and plays.

☐ try to use correct spelling, capitalization, punctuation, grammar, and sentences.

GO ON

Common Core State Standards

CCSS Literature 5. Explain major differences between poems, drama, and prose, and refer to the structural elements of poems (e.g., verse, rhythm, meter) and drama (e.g., casts of characters, settings, descriptions, dialogue, stage directions) when writing or speaking about a text. (Also **CCSS Writing 2.**, **CCSS Writing 4.**, **CCSS Writing 5.**, **CCSS Language 1.**, **CCSS Language 2.**)

_____

_____

_____

_____

_____

_____

_____

_____

_____

_____

_____

_____

_____

_____

_____

_____

_____

_____

_____

_____

_____

_____

VOCABULARY

Directions

Find the word or words with the same meaning as the underlined word. Circle the letter next to the answer.

1 They are <u>astronauts</u>.

(A) travelers in outer space

B scientists who study plants

C people who build trains

D visitors from another state

2 We use the <u>lunar</u> calendar.

F related to the stars

(G) related to the moon

H related to the planets

J related to the sun

3 The <u>module</u> needs several repairs.

A switch

B surface

C shudder

(D) section

4 The <u>hatch</u> blew open.

(F) covered entrance

G air passageway

H locked cabinet

J water barrel

5 Mr. Stein is looking at the <u>horizon</u>.

A location of planets as they move around the sun

B pattern of unusual lights that streak across the sky

(C) place where the sky seems to meet the earth

D features that appear on the surface of the moon

6 I sat alone in the <u>capsule</u>.

F part of an attic

G part of an office

(H) part of a rocket

J part of a school

7 They had to <u>quarantine</u> the plants.

(A) separate

B display

C harvest

D process

GO ON

Common Core State Standards

Questions 1–7: CCSS Foundational Skills 4.c. Use context to confirm or self-correct word recognition and understanding, rereading as necessary.

WORD ANALYSIS

Directions

For each sentence, choose the correct meaning of the underlined word. Circle the letter next to the answer.

8 Brad took a class in <u>astronomy</u>.

    F study of science fiction

    G study of living things

    H study of air flight

    (J) study of heavenly bodies

9 I enjoy reading the <u>astrology</u> column in the newspaper.

    A study of science and technology

    (B) study of how the planets may influence life on Earth

    C study of how people travel from place to place

    D study of health and nutrition

10 We saw an <u>astrolabe</u> in the museum.

    F old instrument used in measuring distance

    (G) old instrument use to find the position of stars

    H old instrument used in telling time

    J old instrument used in steering a ship

11 The <u>astronomer</u> attended the conference.

    (A) person who studies stars

    B person who names new types of trees

    C person who disputes horoscopes

    D person who builds ships

12 It was fun to watch the <u>lunar</u> eclipse.

    (F) having to do with the moon

    G having to do with clouds

    H having to do with the sun

    J having to do with the seasons

GO ON

Common Core State Standards

Questions 8–12: **CCSS Language 4.b.** Use common, grade-appropriate Greek and Latin affixes and roots as clues to the meaning of a word (e.g., *telegraph, photograph, autograph*).

COMPREHENSION

Oceans

Oceans are large bodies of water that cover more than seventy percent of Earth's surface. While there are many seas, lakes, and rivers in the world, there are only five oceans.

The Pacific is the largest ocean. It covers about one-third of Earth. It is so big that all of the land on Earth could fit into it! The Atlantic Ocean is also large. It is perhaps the busiest ocean for trade. Many ships filled with goods sail across it between Europe and the Americas.

The Indian Ocean is much smaller than the Pacific and Atlantic. It has mostly calm waters except when storms called *typhoons* appear. The Arctic Ocean is the smallest of them all. It sits at the top of the world. It is very cold. Ice covers this ocean for much of the year. In the summer, the ice melts and breaks up into pieces that float on the water. They are called floes.

The Southern Ocean is a new ocean. It was named by scientists in the year 2000. It is made up of parts of other oceans. The Southern Ocean surrounds the continent of Antarctica. Like the Arctic Ocean, it is very cold and has ice.

The oceans of the world provide us with food and water. We get around by crossing them. Many people live along their coasts. Without the oceans, life on Earth would not exist. But we still have many things to learn about oceans. The bottom of the ocean floor is largely unexplored. Perhaps one day in the future we will know everything about the oceans of the world.

Oceans of the World

Ocean	Area in square miles	Deepest Point in feet
Arctic	5,405	15,305
Atlantic	29,637,973	28,231
Indian	26,469,600	23,812
Pacific	60,060,893	35,837
Southern	7,864,900	23,737

Source: *New York Times Almanac 2006,* p. 455

GO ON

Directions

Choose the item that best answers each question about the selection you just read. Circle the letter next to the answer.

13 Which ocean is the third largest?

A the Southern Ocean

B the Arctic Ocean

C the Atlantic Ocean

(D) the Indian Ocean

14 How much of Earth's surface is covered by the Pacific Ocean?

F three-quarters

G one-half

(H) one-third

J one-fourth

15 The ocean with the deepest point is

A the Atlantic Ocean.

B the Indian Ocean.

(C) the Pacific Ocean.

D the Arctic Ocean.

16 Which detail does not support the generalization that all the oceans of the world are important to our lives on Earth?

F People get around by crossing oceans.

G Many people live along the coasts of oceans.

H Oceans provide us with food and water.

(J) There are only five oceans on Earth.

17 How much larger is the area of the Atlantic Ocean than the Pacific Ocean?

A about 3,000 square miles

B about 30,000 square miles

C about 300,000 square miles

(D) about 30,000,000 square miles

18 Which two oceans have nearly the same depth?

F the Indian and Arctic Oceans

G the Atlantic and Pacific Oceans

H the Arctic and Southern Oceans

(J) the Indian and Southern Oceans

19 Floes are

(A) floating pieces of ice.

B ice that covers an ocean.

C ships on water.

D land masses.

20 What information is not shown on the chart?

F ocean names

G ocean areas

(H) explorers of each ocean

J each ocean's deepest point

GO ON

Common Core State Standards

Questions 13, 15, 17–18, 20: CCSS Informational Text 7. Interpret information presented visually, orally, or quantitatively (e.g., in charts, graphs, diagrams, time lines, animations, or interactive elements on Web pages) and explain how the information contributes to an understanding of the text in which it appears. **Questions 14, 16, 19: CCSS Informational Text 3.** Explain events, procedures, ideas, or concepts in a historical, scientific, or technical text, including what happened and why, based on specific information in the text.

WRITTEN RESPONSE TO THE SELECTION

> **Look Back and Write** Look back at page 456. Alone in the spacecraft, Michael Collins had many jobs to do. What were they? Why was it so important that he was well prepared to carry out these responsibilities?

The information in the box below will help you remember what you should think about when you write your composition.

REMEMBER—YOU SHOULD

☐ explain the responsibilities Michael Collins had on the spacecraft and why it was so important to be well prepared to carry them out.

☐ use descriptive language to create a word picture of Michael Collins on the spacecraft.

☐ tell what difficulties he faced clearly so that the reader understands what you are saying.

☐ try to use correct spelling, capitalization, punctuation, grammar, and sentences.

GO ON

Common Core State Standards

CCSS Writing 2.b. Develop the topic with facts, definitions, concrete details, quotations, or other information and examples related to the topic. (Also **CCSS Informational Text 3.**, **CCSS Writing 2.**, **CCSS Writing 4.**, **CCSS Writing 5.**, **CCSS Language 1.**, **CCSS Language 2.**)